BEGINNINGS
the Sacred Design

To Rhys,
a man seeking
Answers to the eternal questions.

Best Wishes

Jonathan

Christmas 1996

Dedicated to my son,
Gene

Foreword

Most of us have an inherent fascination for and curiosity about beginnings. Scientists, physicists, cosmologists, archaeologists, historians and theologians have spent lifetimes searching for our origins–the origins of man, our Earth, our Solar System, our Universe. This book is a search into those beginnings–a search from a *different* perspective. In piecing together the evidence, a pattern emerges–a design that appears to be interwoven into all things. Such a master design speaks eloquently of a Master Designer.

This work is the fruit of many years of study and research, and correspondence with others who share the same passion for understanding. My special thanks goes to my friend, Neil Pinter, author of *The Eternal Question: Does God Exist?* Our continuing correspondence and sharing of research has opened many things to my awareness that have contributed to the writing of this book.

My thanks also goes to my husband, Ralph, for his continual encouragement, and for his listening ear when I overflow with excitement for the beauty of these concepts.

Most of all, my heartfelt gratitude must be expressed to a loving and patient Heavenly Father. This study has greatly strengthened my faith and helped me to realize His infinite beauty and majesty.

Bonnie Gaunt
Jackson, Michigan,
April, 1995

CONTENTS

1
Beginnings

I remember once, when I was just a little girl, asking my mother, "Where did I come from?" I was five, but the awareness of the need for beginnings comes to us at a young age.

My mother's answer was straight forward and simplistic, as any honest parent would be with a five-year-old. "You came from your mother and father."

I knew that. But that was not really the burden of my question. "But where did you come from—and your mother—and her mother—and her mother?"

Five-year-olds can be exasperating, but they are capable of some profound thinking. I wanted to know where we *all* came from.

My mother wiped her hands on her apron and paused, searching within herself for all the wisdom of the ages that could be condensed into a few honest, meaningful words to be comprehended by a five-year-old. Finally the answer came, "We all came from God."

I processed that for a moment. It was not satisfactory. It did not answer my question—loose ends were still dangling.

"But where did God come from?"

Her audible sigh could be felt more loudly than heard. "If I told you who made God, then you'd want to know who made *him,* and who made *him,* and who made *him.* Why don't we just stop with God!" The irritableness in her voice told me that it was time to pursue other quests.

It is not within the grasp of a five-year-old to imagine something that did not have a beginning. In fact, fifty-five-year-olds are still grappling with it.

For centuries, the world's leading physicists and cosmologists have spent lifetimes in search of beginnings. The great debate of the current century divides physicists between *beginnings* and *no beginnings*. Did the universe have a beginning, or did it always exist?

But the inquisitive little girl began to grow up. I remember a science textbook that was issued to me in junior high school. I liked science, but I especially liked to look at the pictures. I vividly remember a picture of the "beginning" of things—it showed the Sun spinning and flinging off pieces of itself which swirled around and became planets. Kind of like a wet dog swishing the water off its coat.

No kidding! This was really in my science textbook. I sincerely hope that the students today in that rural southern school have been issued new science books.

So much for the wet dog theory. Yet, from our vantage point here on Earth, we see the Sun as the biggest and brightest thing up there, and we are aware that it is the source of light, heat, and the possibility of life on this earth.

This vital dependence upon the Sun for our existence has led many people in many cultures and ages to think of the Sun as the supreme deity—their source of life.

Even though today, we know that our Sun is merely a medium sized star, tucked away in a remote corner of a huge galaxy, which itself is remotely tucked away in a vast Universe of galaxies, yet, we are very aware of the importance of the Sun to life on Earth. The Sun is not our creator, though it appears to be. The simile is important to our understanding of beginnings.

Our present day knowledge of the workings of the Universe had a beginning nearly four hundred years ago with Galileo. Later, Newton contributed mightily to our understanding. At the beginning of the 20th century, Albert Einstein expanded our awareness with his special theory of relativity, in 1905. Later, in 1915, he expanded the scope of his concepts into what is now known as general relativity and gravity. In 1926, the theory of quantum mechanics gave us deeper insight into the work of beginnings.

In 1929, Edwin Hubble discovered that the Universe was expanding. This presupposed that there must have been a singularity from which the expansion began. Thus we had the birth of the Big Bang theory.

We've come a long way from wet dog to the Big Bang. But physicists and cosmologists are still searching for a unified theory that will explain everything in the Universe, including its origin. They call it TOE (theory of everything).

Musing on the concept of TOE, Cambridge University Professor Stephen Hawking said:

> ...there should exist a set of laws that completely determines the evolution of the universe from its initial state. These laws may have been ordained by God.[1]

Religion and science have a common goal in the ancient human quest for the origin and purpose of life. Only in mod-

---

1 Stephen Hawking, *Black Holes and Baby Universes,* Bantam Books, 1993, p. 128. (Quoted by permission of Bantam Books.)

ern times has there been an attempt to separate the two. And for this separation we are the poorer.

The Bible begins with a very scientific statement: *"In the beginning God created the heavens and the earth."* It leaves no question as to a first cause.

Albert Einstein drew the universe together in a simple formula: $E = mc^2$, or, energy is mass times the speed of light squared. This formula, as usually written, is for the obtaining of energy (E) from the multiplication of mass (m) and light (c). It can just as properly be converted to $m = E \div c^2$ which now tells us that mass (or matter) can be produced by dividing energy (E) by the speed of light squared (c^2). Essentially it is the formula for creation. Thus the two prerequisites for the creation of matter are energy and light.

If then, all matter is energy divided by the speed of light squared, where does the energy and light come from? Where did the Creator get his raw materials? The only answer left is that they came from within.

The transmission of light through space was the key to relativity. However, it was the emission and absorption of light by matter that became the foundation of the quantum theory. Through quantum physics we have been able to come to an understanding of the fundamentals of all matter, including light. Succinctly stated, light is electromagnetic energy in transit. It is a traveling wave of electromagnetic energy.

Long before quantum physics, we knew that matter was composed of tiny particles which are called *atoms*. It was once thought that atoms were the smallest division of matter. Our very word *atom* is from a Greek term meaning undivided. The quantum theory has rendered the name obsolete. Atoms can indeed be divided into protons, neutrons, electrons, and quarks, (not to mention leptons, mesons, and superstrings). Quarks are a thousand times smaller than the protons and neutrons they inhabit, and a hundred million times smaller than the once indivisible atom.

Electrons and quarks are called point particles, which by definition have no size nor extension in space. That is, of course, a physical impossibility—it is only statistical.

If we can get around the "size" problem, what are elementary particles made of? Is there anything of substance down there?

In 1911, Ernest Rutherford proposed a model for the atom which resembled a planet orbiting the Sun. Yet the tiny nucleus in the heart of the atom remained a mystery. The nucleus is one ten-thousandth the size of a whole atom, and it can, in turn, be broken down into simpler components, protons and neutrons.

The proton was already known as a simple nucleus of the hydrogen atom, but in 1932, James Chadwick discovered the neutron. Neutrons are found in the nucleus of all atoms except the hydrogen atom. Their function is to give stability to the nucleus. The hydrogen atom, however, needs no support for its stability.

In every atom there are always the same number of protons as there are electrons. The number of neutrons, however, varies. In nature there are 92 basic atoms. Man has now been able to "create" new elements by adding protons and electrons. Plutonium, the 94th element, is the most poisonous substance known to man, and was created by man for the purpose of destruction.

Hydrogen, the only atom that does not need neutrons to hold it together, is probably the most interesting of all, and gives us an insight into the basic foundation of creation.

When two hydrogen atoms approach each other, their combined energy becomes lower if they share their electron. This lower energy is always sought at the atomic level. The joining of two hydrogen atoms forms the hydrogen molecule. The reason for the lower energy and greater stability of the hydrogen molecule is that by sharing, the electron waves overlap in the region between the two protons. This gives a greater negative charge between the two positively charged protons and bonds them together. This overlapping of the electrons in the hydrogen atom is a function basic to the whole concept of creation. It can be shown graphically by the following diagram:

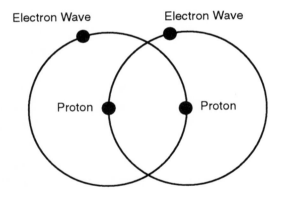

The design is basic to creation, and to the Creator!

Of all the cosmic matter in the Universe, 92% is hydrogen. Our Sun is mostly a ball of hydrogen. The weight of its mass, under the pull of its own gravity, raises its internal temperature to 15 million °C. (Remember the 15 million—it is an

important number relating to the Sun, as will be shown later.)
The heat causes the two nuclei to fuse into one. Instead of two
atoms of hydrogen, we now have one atom of helium. In the
process, a small amount of the mass in each hydrogen nucleus
is converted into pure energy ($E = mc^2$). It is this energy that
heats and lights our Solar System, and is the reason that life
can exist on Earth.

The Sun was god to many peoples throughout history
because it was the source of light, warmth, and life. It glows
red in the sky, and its brilliance is such that a man cannot look
upon it, except as through the more dense atmospheric effect
close to the horizon. It is indeed a fitting symbol of God—an
apparently intended symbol. And it is this symbol that I want
to talk about.

The first verse of the book of Genesis covers the whole
of the created universe. *"In the beginning God (Elohim) created the heavens and the earth."* The word "God" here is mis-
leading; the Hebrew word is אלהים *(Elohim),* which is a plural
word. The singular form is אל, *El.*

This singular form is used in Psalm 90:2, *"From everlasting to everlasting thou art God (El),"* implying that there
was a time before *El* was *Elohim.*

How did *El* become *Elohim?* Let's look at the symbol.
The hydrogen atom with its one proton in its nucleus is the
beginning of all creation. All other atoms are made by the
addition of protons and electrons. Hydrogen is basic, it is the
foundation of the building blocks of creation. It aptly represents *El.*

If *El* were *"from everlasting to everlasting"* it would
imply no beginning and no ending—a concept we have diffi-
culty comprehending. Think of it as a circle. This is what char-

7

acterized the hydrogen atom, it's nucleus was one proton orbited by one electron, forming a circle. A circle is Unity, having no beginning nor ending.

In the New Testament we are told that the Son of God is *"the image of the invisible God, the firstborn of every creature."* In other words, he was exactly like the Father, and the first one made. It could be illustrated like this:

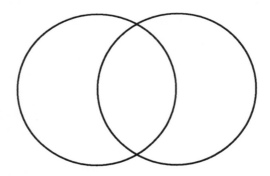

One circle becomes two by division. The second becomes the image of the first—the *El* becoming the *Elohim.* This was the active principle in the creation of matter. If the hydrogen atom, with its one proton, represents *El,* then the hydrogen molecule, which is the division of one into two, represents *Elohim.* It is the fusion of the two atoms of the hydrogen molecule that creates the massive amounts of heat and light which comes from the Sun. The fusion, or unity of the Father and Son become the one source of all creation.

This principle of growth by division was the active principle in the creation of all matter. Each of the elements of which all matter is composed is identified by the number of protons in its nucleus—all divisions of, and consequently exact replicas of the one in the hydrogen atom.

The life-giving heat and light from the Sun is a visual symbol of the giving of life to plants and animals (including man) on the earth. And the duality of the life-giver is clearly shown in Genesis 1:26: *"And Elohim said, 'Let us make man in our image, after our likeness.'"* The Hebrew pronouns used are definitely plural, indicating that *Elohim* was also plural. The same idea is made even more evident in the next verse: *"So Elohim made man in his own image, in the image of Elohim created he him; male and female created he them."* By creating man in the image of *Elohim,* man was made in a dual nature—male and female. Again the dual nature of man is shown in Genesis 5:2: *"Male and female created he them; and blessed them, and called their name Adam (אדם, man)."*

The overlapping circles of the hydrogen atom represent Unity in the midst of becoming dual—*El* becoming *Elohim.* The third figure that is formed by the overlapping of the circles of this "growth by division" was a figure used by early Christians as a symbol of Christ. It looked like the body of a fish. Therefore it has been named the Vesica Piscis. The sign of the fish is still used by Christians today.

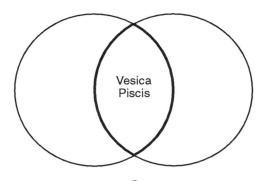

Vesica Piscis

The overlapping circles of the hydrogen molecule are basic to an understanding of creation. This subject will be dealt with in depth later in this study, but first, to establish the scientific fact of creation, we must take a look at the supposed conflict of Genesis One.

2
The Conflict of Genesis One

The first chapter of Genesis has become a barrier to scientific investigation of the origin of the Universe.

Many well-meaning Christians stand firmly in the position: "My mind is made up, don't confuse me with the facts." While many physicists, on the other hand, stand just as resolutely on the educated platform of: "Genesis is unscientific."

The conflict lies first in the aspect of time. Today's physics can provide evidence that the Universe is about 15 billion years old. It is not a wild guess. It is based on many independent evidences. Genesis One, on the other hand, does the whole job in six days.

The second, and equally important conflict is the existence of a Beginner–a Creator. Christians have no problem with this, it is simply a matter of faith. The physicist, on the other hand, sees all matter as beginning with a singularity that is explained as occurring without a Creator.

I have simplified and polarized the conflict for emphasis. It must be acknowledged, however, that not all Christians and not all physicists are thus polarized. There are physicists who believe that the singularity from which the Universe expanded was a direct creation of an all-wise God, who ordained all the fixed laws that control the Universe. And there are also students of scripture who search for the harmony of science and creation.

The record in Genesis of the origin of the Universe is probably the most colossal understatement known to man. It simply states, *"In the beginning God created the heavens and the earth."*

Is the Genesis story of creation the ultimate metaphor, or is it literal truth? Does it indeed conflict with today's physics? Unless there is ultimate agreement between the two, one or the other would, of course, have to be discarded.

Because most of us were taught the Genesis story as children, some tend to think of it as merely a child's tale, needing to be discarded by the wisdom of adulthood. In reality, the Genesis story is a succinct, but completely scientific account of the beginning of things.

Author and lecturer Gerald L. Schroeder, Ph.D., a graduate from the Massachusetts Institute of Technology, and an applied physicist, summed up his years of study with the cogent statement:

> What was for me the most exciting discovery in this search is that the duration of events of the billions of years that, according to cosmologists, have followed the Big Bang, and those events of the first six days of Genesis are, in fact, one and the same. They are identical realities that have been described in vastly different terms.[1]

---

1 Gerald L. Schroeder, Ph.D., *Genesis and the Big Bang,* Bantam Books, New York, 1992, p. 26. (Quoted by permission of Gerald L. Schroeder.)

He was following the advice of Moses Maimonides, who, in his *Guide for the Perplexed,* written in 1190, suggested:

> Study astronomy and physics if you desire to comprehend the relation between the world and God's management of it.

In recent times we have heard much about the Big Bang theory. Some tend to scoff at it because the name implies perhaps an accident or a mistake; and such an irreverent term could not aptly apply to the work of a *divine* Creator. In reality, the name "Big Bang" was indeed coined in derision, by its opponents. But, because of its descriptive impact, the name stuck.

Astronomer Edwin Hubble was the first to observe the evidence of an expanding Universe. In the late 1920s he was engaged in determining the distances from earth to the stars, by the measurement of their spectra. The method, using a spectroscope, breaks the light from a star into its rainbow of color. In the spectroscope, these rainbow colors appear to be crossed by narrow lines. These lines are as characteristic as fingerprints, and occur at precise wavelengths which can be measured. The spectrum of visible light shows reds at one end and blues at the other end, the reds being the longest wavelengths and the blues being the shortest. Hubble noticed that the whole pattern of lines in the light from distant galaxies is shifted toward the red end of the spectrum. This is known to astronomers as "redshift." It indicated that light no longer had the wavelength that it should have, but it appeared to be stretched. But how? He concluded that it was because they were moving away from us.

It would be expected that if all the galaxies in the Universe were moving at random, they would have about equal redshifts and blueshifts, (blueshift indicates moving closer). But Hubble discovered that beyond our immediate cosmic neighborhood, there are no blueshifts–only redshifts. They are all moving away. The speed at which they are moving away is proportional to the amount of redshift. This is known today as Hubble's Law. Using this law, astronomers had only to measure the redshift to determine the distance of a galaxy. But the dynamic implication of Hubble's Law was that the Universe was expanding.

The reverse of this (looking back in time) would automatically bring us to a time when all the galaxies were close together–and going back further in time would put *no* space between them at all! What then? There must have existed what physicists call a "singularity," in which all of the substance of the Universe was born in a superdense fireball at a definite moment in time.

Measuring the redshift could define that moment in time. Today's best calculations put it at about 15 billion years ago. By comparison, the same cosmologists tell us that our Solar System, including our Earth, is about 5 billion years old.

The Hubble telescope orbiting our Earth, after having its lenses repaired and focused, is said to be able to see to the edge of the Universe. If so, then the 15 billion years for the age of the Universe can be either confirmed or revised.

Following Hubble's discovery of an expanding Universe, the answer to another mystery became clear–why is the night sky dark? As children, we looked up into the sky at night and knew that it was dark because the sun was no longer up there. It had gone down in the west, and light had gone with it. That might be true if there were no other sources of light in the sky.

14

Believe it or not, the dark night sky tells us there is infinite space and therefore infinite time, or more precisely, a point beyond which there is no measurement of time.

If the Universe had existed for infinite time, the night sky would be full of light, because all the light from all the stars and galaxies would have filled all the space. The darkness that we see, between the stars, is actually the edge of time as far as our Universe is concerned, and it lies 15 billion light years away.

John Gribbin, an astrophysicist at Cambridge University stated it simply:

> ...as we move into the high-tech world of radio telescopes and artificial satellites, never forget that the only equipment you need to prove that the Universe was born at a definite moment in time...is your own pair of eyes, looking up at the blackness of the night sky between the stars.[1]

Leftover from the Big Bang is radiation that can be heard and measured, filling all the space between the stars and galaxies. With the expansion of the Universe, the radiation has stretched and cooled, until today it has a wavelength in the microwave band, similar to that in our microwave ovens. It has a temperature of 2.7K (Kelvin).[2] It can be heard in our living rooms when we tune our TV to a frequency between stations. About 1 percent of the static you hear is, in fact, cosmic microwave radiation left over from the Big Bang. This

---

1 John Gribbin, *In The Beginning,* Little, Brown and Company, New York, 1993, p. 16. (Quoted by permission from Little Brown and Company.)

2 Kelvin temperature is an absolute scale, based on thermodynamic principles, in which zero is equivalent to -459.4°F or -273°C.

was confirmed in 1992 by the observing of tiny ripples in the radiation corresponding to minute differences in the temperature of the energy reaching us from different parts of the Universe. It was hailed as one of the major discoveries of the century because it was evidence for the birth of the Universe.

The Hebrew Torah describes it as exactly that—a birth—using the word תולדת, which means birth or origin. The text reads: *"These are the births of the heavens and of the earth when they were created, in the day of the making of Jehovah Elohim's earth and heavens."* (Genesis 2:1)

This brings us back to the problem of the time. The text reads, *"in the day of the making of Jehovah Elohim's earth and heavens."* This follows, or completes, the description of the six days of creation in Genesis 1. In this summary statement, it places the whole process of the birth and development of the Universe into one "day." This is not a contradiction in terms. In fact, it contributes to an understanding of the six days that had just been described.

To the realist, however, we are not only confronted with the problem of squeezing 15 billion years into six days, we are now forced to condense it all into one day. The Genesis account not only appears to be a contradiction of itself, it hands us the Herculean task of reconciling the biblical data with seemingly vastly different cosmological evidence.

It is difficult to think of time in terms outside our own experience. We tend to think of the steady flow of time as a constant. It is possible, however, that the Creator's concept of time could be vastly different from ours. This is suggested in the Psalm of David: *"A thousand years in your eyes are as a day that passes,"* (Psalm 90:4). David was not, however, talking about actual time measurement, but only the relative perception of it. This we are familiar with, for, as we all know time seems to pass more quickly when we are having fun than when we are having a tooth pulled. However, the empirically observed reality of Einstein's law of relativity tells us that the passage of time is not an absolute.

Before Einstein, time was always considered as an absolute. Isaac Newton said, "Absolute, true and mathematical time, of itself, and from its own nature, flows equably without relation to anything external."[1]

If time is relative to the observer, who was there to measure the passage of time prior to the appearance of man? Who was watching the clock?

What clock do we use to measure time? Today we use the seeming constant of Earth's relationship to the Sun and sometimes the Moon, stars and planets. The interwoven relationship of these orbs forms our working clock. Yet, when God alone was watching the clock, these orbs did not yet exist.

Stephen Hawking, in *Black Holes and Baby Universes,* suggested that there was a point before which time did not exist.

> It used to be considered obvious that time flowed on forever, regardless of what was happening; but the theory of relativity combined time with space and said that both could be warped, or distorted, by the matter and energy in the Universe. So our perception of the nature of time changed from being independent of the Universe to being shaped by it. It then became con-

---

1 Isaac Newton, *Mathematical Principles and Natural Philosophy.*

ceivable that time might simply not be defined before a certain point...."[1]

Genesis 1:1 is a general statement of overview of the works of creation, but verse 2 begins by saying that *"the earth was without form and empty."* The two poetic Hebrew words used here are *tohu* and *bohu*. They both have the same meaning but are placed together poetically for emphasis. They mean "empty space, without form, nothing, void, desolation." Today's particle physicists refer to T and B (*tohu* and *bohu*) as the emptiness that was compressed by the forces of the Big Bang, converting the primordial hydrogen into helium, and from there into the rest of the elements. Thus in the beginning of "day one" the Sun and our Earth had not yet come into existence. God was not operating on solar time. Nor is there any way we can time creation with a solar clock.

Why, then, is the account of creation stated as six days—six divisions. What was the purpose of dividing it at all? Possibly the division into six parts had a deeper significance than time. But why six?

Six is unique. It is the only number that is both the sum and product of its parts: by adding $1 + 2 + 3$ or by multiplying $1 \times 2 \times 3$ the answer is 6. The number 6 is called the "perfect" number because it is equal to the sum of its factors. Very few numbers have this quality. The next perfect number is 28. Only 23 perfect numbers have ever been found, and 6 is the first one.

The first Hebrew word in Genesis 1 is *breshith,* בראשית. It is really two words because in Hebrew the preposition *in* is

---

1 Stephen Hawking, *Black Holes and Baby Universes,* Bantam Books, New York, 1992, p. 46. (Quoted by permission of Bantam Books.)

usually attached to the word it is placing, rather than our English way of writing it separately. *Breshith* is translated *"In the beginning."* (*The* is added by the translators–the literal translation is *"In beginning."*) The term *breshith* is actually a play on words, from the two Hebrew words, *bara shith,* which means "created six." The Hebrew word *bara* is the word used for *Creator* in the Old Testament. The word *shith,* (sometimes *sheth*), is the Hebrew word שת, which means six. Thus creation, Creator, and six are inseparably connected in the first word of the Bible–*breshith*– *"In the beginning."*

Perhaps time is not so much the question as is the importance and significance of the number six.

Before pursuing this possibility, it is first important to observe the use of numbers in the harmony of the Universe, then perhaps the division of six will fall into its natural place.

3
The Case for a Designer

An understanding of both physics and biblical tradition shows that the opening chapters of the book of Genesis and the findings of modern cosmology corroborate rather than dispute each other.

(Gerald L. Schroeder, Ph.D.)[1]

Dr. Schroeder went on to say, "Theology devoid of knowledge of the physical universe is a contradiction in terms."

John Gribbin, in his book *In The Beginning,*[2] posed the obvious ultimate question–"Where did the Big Bang come from?"

Gribbin, an astrophysicist at Cambridge University, makes a strong case for the correctness of the Big Bang theory, showing the infinite balance in its every aspect. His observations and analyses brought him, naturally, to question causes–first causes. Chapter seven of his book, *In The Beginning,* addresses a reality that all who study the subject must face–

---

1 Gerald L. Schroeder, Ph.D., *Genesis and the Big Bang,* Bantam Books, New York, 1990, p. 10. (Quoted by permission from Gerald L. Schroeder.)

2 John Gribbin, *In the Beginning,* Little, Brown and Company, New York, 1993, p. 20. (Quoted by permission from Little Brown and Company.)

the enigma of chance in the face of order and design. He suggested that "All apparent coincidences of cosmology are neither extraordinary nor accidental, but are the natural result of the processes that gave birth to the Universe." He called it the Goldilocks principle–that just like Baby Bear's porridge, the Universe is "just right." But what, or who, made it just right? Gribbin muses, "Has the cosmic porridge been lovingly cooked up by a cosmic chef who knows what Goldilocks likes?"

To that I will answer with an emphatic "yes!"

Fred Hoyle, one of the opponents of the Big Bang theory (and reported as the one who thought up the name), is also reported as having said "A commonsense interpretation of the facts suggests that a superintellect has monkeyed with physics, as well as chemistry and biology, and there are no blind forces worth speaking about in nature."

Cosmologist George Smoot, in his delightful book, *Wrinkles in Time,*[1] sums it up succinctly (page 291):

> Go back further still, beyond the moment of creation–what then? What was there before the big bang?...Facing this, the ultimate question, challenges our faith in the power of science to find explanations of nature. The existence of a singularity–in this case the given, unique state from which the universe emerged– is anathema to science, because it is beyond explanation.... Is this, then, where scientific explana-

---

1 George Smoot, *Wrinkles in Time,* William Morrow and Company, Inc., New York, 1993. (George Smoot discovered the ripples in the cosmic background radiation, thereby confirming the Big Bang concept, and the ability of the balance between gravity and expansion to stabilize, permitting the Universe to exist indefinitely.) (Quoted by permission of William Morrow and Company, Inc.)

tion breaks down and God takes over, the artificer of that singularity, that initial simplicity? The astrophysicist Robert Jastrow, in his book *God and the Astronomers,* described such a prospect as the scientist's nightmare: "He has scaled the mountains of ignorance; he is about to conquer the highest peak; as he pulls himself over the final rock, he is greeted by a band of theologians who have been sitting there for centuries."

In reality, we need be neither a physicist nor a theologian to observe the abundance of evidence that we see every day.

I remember walking the beach at St. Augustine, Florida one April morning. I wanted to watch the sunrise over the Atlantic Ocean. It was a delightful morning, and the first glow of sunlight caught the spray from the heavy surf and turned it to bursts of gold. I watched to the east, out beyond the endless Atlantic, as the full orb of the Sun gently came into view. Then I turned and looked to the west where the beautiful full Moon was still hanging, as if it were waiting for the Sun to take its turn in giving us light. A marvellous sight—the sun glowing a deep red, and the full moon shedding its translucent silver.

From where I stood, there on the beach, both orbs looked to be the same size. Yet I knew that the Sun was much further away and much larger than the Moon.

In reality, the Sun is precisely 400 times larger than the Moon. It would take 400 Moons, lined up side by side, to reach across the diameter of the Sun. But look up into the sky, and they appear to be the same size. Was the relationship by chance, or was it part of a grand design?

Because of this precise size-relationship, when the Moon comes between the Earth and the Sun we have a total eclipse of the Sun. The full orb of the Moon completely covers the full orb of the Sun, while the shadow of the Moon reaches precisely to the Earth, coming to a point at Earth's surface. Such precision, over such distances, does not seem likely to be the result of blind chance. It speaks loudly of design. Where there is design, there must be a designer.

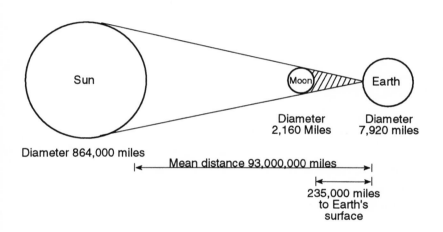

Diameter 864,000 miles

Diameter
2,160 Miles

Diameter
7,920 miles

Mean distance 93,000,000 miles

235,000 miles
to Earth's
surface

Throughout man's experience on this Earth, we have only seen one side of the Moon. The Moon's rotation on its axis is carefully synchronized with its monthly orbit of Earth, so that the same face is always seen from Earth. Such a precise relationship that involves size, speed of rotation, plane of rotation, and distance, is not likely the result of chance.

23

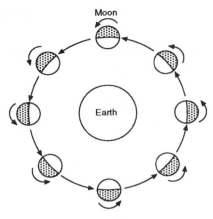

In the first chapter of Genesis we are told that the Sun and Moon were to be for "signs, for seasons, for days and for years." Of course we use the Sun and Moon for the precise determining of the length of seasons, days and years, but let's examine their purpose as "signs."

During the Moon's complete orbit of Earth, it traces a path that is the length of 720 of its diameters. In other words, if we replicated the Moon and placed them side by side in the orbital path, we would need 720 Moons to precisely fill the path.

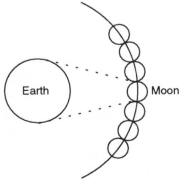

THE CASE FOR A DESIGNER

The importance of the numbers in the design begins to make itself apparent. The diameters of the Sun, Earth and Moon are evenly divisible by 720–it is the largest number that will divide them evenly.

$$720 \times 12 = 8,640(00) \text{ miles, diameter of Sun}$$
$$720 \times 11 = 7,920 \text{ miles, diameter of Earth}$$
$$720 \times 3 = 2,160 \text{ miles, diameter of Moon}$$

The three multipliers, 12, 11 and 3 are also basic to the design of all the structures of nature, including music, as we shall see later.

The relationship of the sizes of Earth and Moon is precisely the relationship of 3 to 11.

$$11 \div 3 = 3.6666$$
$$7,920 \div 2,160 = 3.6666$$

If the same relationship were applied to the Sun it would point to something out there 3.6666 times its size, namely, 3,168,000 miles. However, if we drew a square around the circle of the Earth, the perimeter of that square would be 31,680 miles.

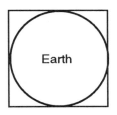

Perimeter of square, 31,680 miles

BEGINNINGS

Draw a square around the Moon and its perimeter will be 8,640 miles, or $^1/_{100}$ the diameter of the Sun. Or, stated in an ancient unit used in the construction of the megalithic sites in Britain, which today has been named the megalithic mile (2.72727272 miles, or 14,400 feet), the perimeter of the square around the Moon would be 3,168 MMi.

Perimeter of square 8,640 miles
Perimeter of square 3,168 MMi.

The cosmological relationship of this ancient unit of measure to the British mile used today shows the harmonious design of the Earth, Sun and Moon.

Diameter of Earth .... 7,920 British Miles
Diameter of Moon .... 792 Megalithic Miles

Perimeter of a square containing
the circle of the earth .... 31,680 British Miles
Perimeter of a square containing
the circle of the Moon .... 3,168 Megalithic Miles

Diameter of the Sun .... 316,800 Megalithic Miles

These relationships are startling. Why are the numbers so inter-related, and why do they point to the number 3,168?

Numbers are a special kind of language–a precise language that loses nothing in translation. The ancient Pythagoras, the 5th century B.C. mathematician, said, "Numbers are the language of the Universe." And he taught his students their importance as a language–a language that communicates through time and space. An external language–a language of beginning.

The ancient Plato perceived the language of numbers and some of its messages planted in the Universe, for he wrote, "God ever geometrizes." Sir James Jeans, the British physicist, declared, "The Great Architect of the Universe now begins to appear as a pure mathematician."

In the writings of the ancient philosophers there is common agreement that the purpose of number is for the investigation of the Universe. And just as the Great Architect spread the vast expanse of the heavens by number, so too his written word can be reduced to number; and those who have tried it have stood in awe of the intricacy and beauty of the design. It was an intentional design.

The Old Testament was written in Hebrew (as well as a few other languages). Hebrew is probably the oldest language known to man. It was a "dual character system"–a meaning of sound and a meaning of number.

The New Testament was also written in a dual character system–the Greek language. Thus each letter of their alphabet represents a number. The Greeks called the system *gematria.*

Gematria among the Greeks was in common use at the time of the writing of the New Testament, thus giving meaning to numbers, and numbers to names, places and things.

The Greek and Hebrew number systems were so similar it becomes obvious that they are of one design.

Greek Gematria

Alpha	α	1
Beta	β	2
Gamma	γ	3
Delta	δ	4
Epsilon	ε	5
Zeta	ζ	7
Eta	η	8
Theta	θ	9
Iota	ι	10
Kappa	κ	20
Lambda	λ	30
Mu	μ	40
Nu	ν	50
Xi	ξ	60
Omicron	ο	70
Pi	π	80
Rho	ρ	100
Sigma	σ ς	200
Tau	τ	300
Upsilon	υ	400
Phi	φ	500
Chi	χ	600
Psi	ψ	700
Omega	ω	800

Hebrew Gematria

Aleph	א	1
Beyth	ב	2
Giymel	ג	3
Daleth	ד	4
He	ה	5
Vav	ו	6
Zayin	ז	7
Cheyth	ח	8
Teyth	ט	9
Yowd	י	10
Kaph	ך כ	20
Lamed	ל	30
Mem	ם מ	40
Nuwn	ן נ	50
Camek	ס	60
Ayin	ע	70
Pe	ף פ	80
Tsadey	ץ צ	90
Qowph	ק	100
Reysh	ר	200
Siyn	ש	300
Tav	ת	400

THE CASE FOR A DESIGNER

Note that in the Greek system the numbers 6 and 90 are omitted. Actually those letter-numbers became obsolete and were dropped from use.

In the Hebrew system there are five letters that are written differently when they occur at the end of a word. These are called finals. The Cabala assigns additional numbers to these finals; however, such a practice was not part of the original letter-number system, but was a later addition. In the original language of the Old Testament, the finals bore the same number as when the letter occurred within a word.

As an example of how gematria works, let's look at the best known name in the New Testament–the *Lord Jesus Christ*.

K	$=$	20	I	$=$	10	X	$=$	600
υ	$=$	400	η	$=$	8	ρ	$=$	100
ρ	$=$	100	σ	$=$	200	ι	$=$	10
ι	$=$	10	o	$=$	70	σ	$=$	200
o	$=$	70	υ	$=$	400	τ	$=$	300
ς	$=$	200	ς	$=$	200	o	$=$	70
		800			888	ς	$=$	200
								1480

Lord (800) + *Jesus* (888) + *Christ* (1480) = 3,168

These are not accidental or chance numbers. Their frequency of use both in the word of God and in the works of God is astounding! They are revealing some of the meaning of the "signs" promised in Genesis 1.

The number 3,168 becomes a sign. It is displayed in the geometry of our Solar System and it is the name Lord Jesus Christ. The inter-relationship of these numbers is amazing.

There is no way they can be manipulated or contrived–they just are. And they have been there since creation.

$$3,168 = \textit{Lord Jesus Christ}$$

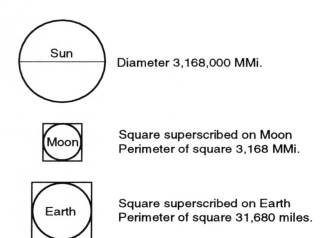

Diameter 3,168,000 MMi.

Square superscribed on Moon
Perimeter of square 3,168 MMi.

Square superscribed on Earth
Perimeter of square 31,680 miles.

Look again at the Sun. Its brilliance is blinding to the comprehension. Its diameter of 864,000 miles can be converted to 456,192 feet (dropping all the zeros).

$$144 \times 3,168 = 456,192$$

Multiply the digits and it equals the diameter of the Moon.

$$4 \times 5 \times 6 \times 1 \times 9 \times 2 = 2,160$$

Add the digits and it resolves to 27–a number that is basic to light and creation, as will be presented later.

$$4 + 5 + 6 + 1 + 9 + 2 = 27$$

Stated in inches it still resolves to 27.

456,192
x   12
5,474,304 $5 + 4 + 7 + 4 + 3 + 0 + 4 = 27$

Just as the Hebrew language reads from right to left, and the Greek language reads from left to right, so the numbers of gematria are similarly interchangeable, because their importance is as numerals, not as quantity. Reading 27 from right to left would change it to 72. In fact, using numbers as numerals even allows them to scramble and retain their meaning.

On page 25 it was shown that the diameters of Earth, Sun and Moon are all evenly divisible by 720, their largest common denominator. The Greek word τοπος *(topos)* has a number equivalent of 720. The meaning of the word describes its importance as the common denominator of Earth, Sun and Moon.

τοπος means "Any portion of space marked off, as it were, from surrounding space." "A portion of space viewed as enclosed or complete in itself." It is sometimes used as a "place." Thus each of the three orbs bears a denominator of 720.

The two numbers, 27 and 72, are basic to light and creation. Put the numbers together to form a palindrome– 027720 –and we have the lowest number evenly divisible by each of the numbers from 1 to 12.

In the gematria of the Old Testament, the number 27 is the number for light. The Hebrew word for light is אור. It adds to 207 and multiplies to 12. Since zeros are merely place holders, it can be written in gematria as 27. The same Hebrew word is sometimes translated *Sun.* The Hebrew word meaning *to illuminate,* יגיד also adds to 27 and multiplies to 12.

In the New Testament the word *seed* is from the Greek word σπορος, meaning that from which life springs. It bears the number 720. The title *Lord God* in Hebrew, יהוה אלהי, also adds to 72. He is that from which life springs.

The relationship of the basic 6 of creation to these numbers is marvelous– 12 x 60 = 720 and 12 + 60 = 72. It begins to look like the work of a Master Mathematician.

And it does not go unnoticed that 2.7k (as shown on page 15) is the temperature of the radiation filling all of space between the stars and galaxies.

In the Old Testament book of Job is recorded some profound questions that God asked Job.

> *Where wast thou when I laid the foundations of the earth? Declare, if thou hast understanding. Who hath laid the measures thereof? Or who hath stretched the line upon it? Whereupon are the foundations thereof fastened? Or who hath laid the cornerstone thereof?*
> (Job 38:4-6)

Apparently the *measures* were important. They were not accidental chance. But look closer. The word *measures* is from the Hebrew word ממדיה which adds to 99. If we multiplied the letter-numbers (dropping all the zeros) it would be 32. The answer to the question *"Who hath laid the measures thereof?"* is in the two numbers, 99 and 32.

$$99 \times 32 = 3,168$$
Lord Jesus Christ = 3,168

A square drawn around the Earth will have a perimeter of 31,680 miles. However, if we placed the Moon tangent to the earth (touching), and enclosed both orbs within a circle, the circumference of the circle would be 31,680 miles (using $^{22}/_7$ for π).

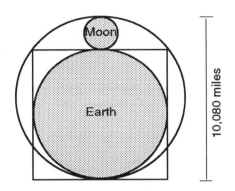

Circumference of circle enclosing
Earth and Moon 31,680 miles.

This use of $^{22}/_7$ for π comes to us from ancient times. Its authenticity is found in gematria.

The name Jesus Christ is spelled two different ways in the Greek text of the New Testament. The letter-numbers of both spellings add to 2,368.

Jesus Christ, Ιησους Χριστος = 2,368
Jesus Christ, Ιησου Χριστου = 2,368
Jesus, Ιησους = 888
Jesus, Ιησου = 688
Christ, Χριστος = 1,480
Christ, Χριστου = 1,680

Using this second spelling for Christ (1,680) we find his relationship to $\pi = {}^{22}/_7$ and the British mile. If we drew a circle one mile in circumference and divided by ${}^{22}/_7$, the diameter would be 1,680, which is *Christ*.

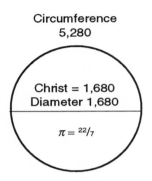

Circumference
5,280

Christ = 1,680
Diameter 1,680

$\pi = {}^{22}/_7$

We saw above that a circle enclosing both Earth and Moon has a circumference of 31,680 miles, using ${}^{22}/_7$ for π. It bears the number for *Lord Jesus Christ*, (3,168). Using that same diagram, we know that the combined radii of Earth and Moon is 5,040 miles (3,960 + 1,080); and the combined diameters are 10,080 miles (7,920 + 2,160). The diagram below shows the relationship of these dimensions to Christ. If we were to multiply the letter-numbers in the two spellings of Christ, they would be:

Christ, Χριστος = 5,040 (zeros dropped)
Christ, Χριστου = 10,080 (zeros dropped)

There is no way it could all be a grand coincidence. It is grand all right, but it was put there by a Grand Creator.

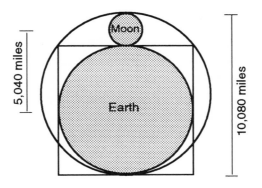

Circumference of circle enclosing
Earth and Moon 31,680 miles.

Lord Jesus Christ (added) = 3,168
Christ, $Χριστου$, added = 1,680, multiplied = 10,080
Christ, $Χριστος$, added = 1,480, multiplied = 5,040

In all the Universe, as far as we know, the only place where terrestrial life exists is in a thin layer that surrounds planet Earth. This thin layer that supports life is within the lithosphere and the atmosphere. The lithosphere (Earth's crust) is an average of ten miles deep. As it surrounds the planet, it can be compared to the skin of an apple in relation to the size of the apple. This is how thin Earth's crust is in relation to the size of the planet. If we stated this 10 miles in inches, it would be 6,336 (dropping all the zeros). The figure is twice 3,168.

Human life is also supported by the atmosphere. It is divided into layers. The troposphere extends upward from sea level approximately seven miles. Beyond that is the stratosphere, going up to twenty two miles. Temperatures in the troposphere decrease with altitude. In the stratosphere they are nearly constant. Above the stratosphere is the mesosphere, with temperatures decreasing with altitude. At fifty miles above sea level, the temperature decrease abruptly stops. It acts as if there were a thin skin surrounding Earth, fifty miles up. This imaginary "skin" is called the mesopause—it is the farthest reaches of Earth's atmosphere. Beyond that is what is known as the thermosphere, because temperatures increase with altitudes. Thus Earth acts as if it were enclosed in a thermal balloon, 50 miles up. Convert those 50 miles to inches, dropping all the zeros, and the result is 3,168.

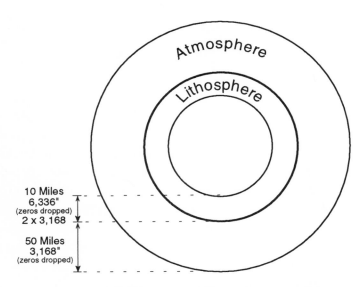

Combined Lithosphere and Atmosphere
50 + 10 = 60 Miles
60 x 5,280 = 316,800 Feet

Lord Jesus Christ, Κυριος Ιησους Χριστος, = 3,168

Thus the thin layer surrounding the Earth that supports life measures three times 3,168.

Earth's biosphere is the only genuinely *living* system, that we know of, in the Universe. No single organism from that biosphere could continue to live outside of it. It is thrilling to realize that its very dimensions tell us of its Maker–the One upon whom life really depends. The combined lithosphere and atmosphere measures 60 miles. Converted to feet it would be stated as 316,800 feet. It is the number of the One of whom John said, *"All things were made by Him,"* (John 1:3) –the *Lord Jesus Christ, Κυριος Ιησους Χριστος* = 3,168.

There are nine planets in our Solar System. The Encyclopedia Britannica lists the mean distances from the Sun to each of these planets (dropping the zeros).

Mercury	36
Venus	67
Earth	93
Mars	142
Jupiter	483
Saturn	886
Uranus	1,782
Neptune	2,793
Pluto	3,672
	9,954

Thus the combined distances from the Sun to each of the nine planets is 9,954. Think of this number as the circumference of a gigantic circle, representing our entire Solar System. Divide by π and we find the diameter to be 3,168. It's as if the Artist's signature has been placed on all His work.

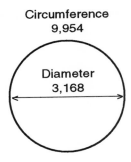

Circumference
9,954

Diameter
3,168

But, you might say, didn't they discover a tenth planet out there beyond Pluto—Planet X? For nearly a hundred years astronomers have been telling us that there is a planet X out beyond Pluto. They have never seen it with their telescopes, but because of the unusual elliptic paths of Neptune and Pluto they knew that a tenth planet was out there somewhere, affecting these orbits.

In the 1950s, some astronomers suggested that instead of an unknown planet beyond Pluto, perhaps there existed a belt of huge ice chunks surrounding the Solar System. They named it the Kuiper belt.

In August of 1992, a tiny reddish spot of light recorded on a sensitive electronic detector in Hawaii became the first component of the Kuiper belt ever observed. The existence of the Kuiper belt was suddenly changed from theory to fact. The new spot of light was named 1992 QB1.

Time magazine (September 28, 1992, p. 59) made the following observation about this discovery:

> Proof that the Kuiper belt exists would help dem-
> onstrate that another long-sought object almost certainly
> does not. For nearly a century, astronomers have been

looking for Planet X, a world conjectured to lie far beyond Pluto.... Planet X was first dreamed up to explain the apparent irregularities in Neptune's orbit. Recent studies have shown those irregularities to be an illusion–and the sighting of QB1 has probably dashed forever the hope of finding a 10th planet.[1]

Yes, 9 completes the planets, just as 9 completes the digits. To mathematicians, 9 is the magic number. It represents completeness–wholeness of a concept–ultimate manifestation of truth. In fact, in the Old Testament the Hebrew word for *perfection* has the number equivalent of 90. Thus the very existence of 9 planets tells us there is not a tenth, for 9 is wholeness.

When the digits in the diameters of the Sun, Earth and Moon are each added, they resolve to 9.

Sun diameter   864,000 (8 + 6 + 4 = 18; 1 + 8 = 9)
Earth diameter   7,920 (7 + 9 + 2 = 18; 1 + 8 = 9)
Moon diameter   2,160 (2 + 1 + 6 = 9)

The sum of the distances from the Sun to each of the 9 planets also resolves to 9 (9 + 9 + 5 + 4 = 27; 2 + 7 = 9). The numbers suggest design. Perhaps the signature of the Designer was given in the first four words of Genesis: *"In the beginning God (Elohim),"* בראשית אלהימ. It adds to 999.

Today, while writing this chapter, I received a letter from my friend, Neil Pinter, author of *The Eternal Question: Does God Exist?* He found, in Webster's New World Dictionary, that the actual distance of Earth's orbit around the Sun covers 595 million miles. This is an elliptical orbit. If the orbit were

---

1 Quoted by permission of Time, Inc., New York, NY

perfectly round, the distance could be simply calculated by doubling the distance from the Sun to the Earth and multiplying by π (not considering the zeros and decimals).

$$595 \times 528 = 314,160$$
$$\pi = 3.1416$$

What a marvellous design! It gives us an awareness of the awesome mind of the Designer—using an ellipse to show the value of π, when π is actually the key to the geometry of a circle! Perhaps it is telling us that even though the orbital path of the Earth around the Sun is an ellipse, mathematically and symbolically it can be treated as a circle.

Let's try treating it as a circle and observe a fantastic design. If it were a circle, the distance from Sun to Earth would be 93 million miles. Convert that to inches, dropping the zeros, and it would be 5,892,480. This is the distance that light travels from the Sun to our Earth. Divide this figure by the speed of light (again dropping the zeros), and the result will be 3,168—the number of the One who was said to be the *"Light of the world."*

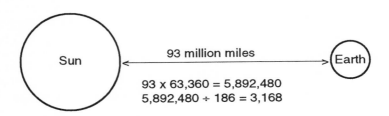

To show the infinite wisdom of the Designer, let's take the same inch measurement from Sun to Earth, and divide it by the circumference of the Earth.

THE CASE FOR A DESIGNER

$$5,892,480 \div 24,881.392 = 2,368$$
Jesus Christ, Ιησους Χριστος = 2,368

The gematria for *Jesus Christ,* 2,368, used as miles in the above calculation can be converted to furlongs by multiplying by 8 (because there are 8 furlongs in a mile).

2,368 miles x 8 = 18,944 furlongs
18,944 x π = 595 (rounding it and dropping zeros)

My friend, Neil Pinter, suggested that we might lay the 595 million miles of Earth's orbit out on a straight line, and then determine the time it would take for light to traverse its length.

595 million miles $\div$ 186 = 3198924.7 seconds
3198924.7 seconds $\div$ 60 = 53315.4 minutes
53315.4 minutes $\div$ 60 = 888 hours
Jesus, Ιησους = 888

It takes light from the Sun 8.3 minutes to reach the Earth. Light from the Sun to the aggregate of the 9 planets in our Solar System takes 107 times 8.3 minutes.

107 x 8.3 = 888
Jesus, Ιησους = 888

Truly the Artist has signed his name to all His works! Such evidence of design reveals the unfathomable mind of the Designer.

In the Autumn of 2 B.C., an event happened that changed the world. Just as had been prophesied by the Hebrew prophets, a baby was born in Bethlehem who was, in reality, the Son of God–the One who was first–the *"only begotten"* of the Father. He came on a special mission, to be the Redeemer of the human race. He was born to a young teenage girl, in a cattle shed in the little village of Bethlehem. Why Bethlehem? Why not the capitol city, Jerusalem? The answer is simple, yet amazing. Look on a globe, or a map of the Middle East and you will find that Bethlehem rests on the latitude of 31.68°N. The Lord Jesus Christ, whose number, 3,168, is planted in the Universe, came to earth and was born precisely on his number– 31.68°N latitude!

As shown previously, the record of Genesis 1 clearly stated that the Sun and Moon were to be for *signs.* These *"two great lights,"* as the Genesis author called them, are indeed signs, pointing to the greatness of their Designer.

The illustration below shows the Moon inscribed within a square. The perimeter of the square becomes the solar number, 864, thus appropriately illustrating that it is one light source. The Moon merely reflects the light of the Sun.

Perimeter of square
8640 – solar number

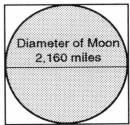

Diameter of Moon
2,160 miles

864 = God, *Θεων (Theon)*

864 = (865[1]) The Sun shines, יזרח שמש, (II Sam. 23:4)

216 = To make light, האיר

---

1 In gematria, one or two units, known as colel, may be added to or subtracted from the value of any word without affecting its meaning.

The Sun is connected to a sign with which we are all familiar–the 12 signs of the Zodiac. These signs have come down to us from ancient times. It has been suggested by Joseph A. Seiss[1] that the names and meanings of the zodiacal signs were given to Adam, Seth and Enoch, by the Creator.

These signs are basically 12, with three more for each, making a total of 48. The Sun, in its annual course from west to east through the constellations, passes through the 12, on what is called the path of the ecliptic. During that time, the Moon makes 12 complete revolutions around the Earth. However, the Sun, at a given point of time in the year, will gradually slip back along the ecliptic path, and in 2,160 years will pass into the zone of the preceding zodiacal sign. This is called the precession of the equinoxes. This phenomenon is due to the tilt of Earth's axis and the slow wobble of its rotation. Thus the Sun remains in each sign of the Zodiac for 2,160 years; and the complete circuit would take 25,920 years.

$12 \times 2,160 = 25,920$ years
$1 \times 2 \times 2 \times 1 \times 6 \times 2 \times 5 \times 9 \times 2 = 4,320$
Radius of Sun $= 432,000$ miles
$432 = $ *All things (Universe),* $\pi\alpha\nu\tau\alpha$

Let them be for signs, and for seasons, and for days and years. (Genesis 1:14)

The above statement is, itself, a revealing of the meaning of the signs. Its total number value is 1,306–the number given to the One who was to be named Emmanuel, which, by interpretation means *"God with us,"* $\mu\varepsilon\theta\ \eta\mu\omega\nu\ o\ \Theta\varepsilon o\varsigma$. The

1   Joseph A. Seiss, *Gospel in the Stars,* Kregel Publications, Grand Rapids, MI, 1972, p. 151.

letter-numbers add to 1,306. The Sun and Moon were the signs. Observe the amazing relationship to Emmanuel.

$$\text{Sun, } \eta\lambda\iota o\varsigma = \quad 318$$
$$\text{Moon, } \sigma\epsilon\lambda\eta\nu\eta = \underline{301}$$
$$619$$

Circumference 619

Diameter 197

Emmanuel, עמנו אל = 197

The Sun and the Moon are thus intricately interwoven into a pattern of time, dimension, function, symbol and number. The *two great lights* are indeed signs–pointing to a marvelous master Architect.

Stand in the sunshine and feel the vibrant radiance of its warmth–its life force–invigorate your body and your spirit. Walk softly through the moonlight and feel the serenity of its silver essence, gently, quietly, soothing the soul. They are God's gifts; and they are evidence of a Master Designer.

4
The Formula for Creation

The book of Genesis begins with the statement, *"In the beginning God created the heaven and the earth."* The Hebrew word translated *"God"* in this text is *Elohim,* a plural word, implying a deity of more than one.

In chapter 1 I showed the diagram of the overlapping circles of the hydrogen molecule and suggested that it was basic to an understanding of creation; and stated that I would return to this concept. I felt it was first necessary to acquaint the reader with the principles of gematria and the evidences of its use in the geometry of our Solar System. This sacred number code, established for us in the Hebrew and Greek scriptures, provides a depth of insight into the work of creation. It reveals a beautiful harmony between the Creator and the created.

I believe, along with Nahmanides (1194-1270), that an understanding of the origins of the Universe must include the biblical account of creation as received by Moses.

In his *Commentary on Genesis,* Nahmanides stated that everything that was given to Moses was written in the Torah explicitly or by implication in the numerical value of the letters.

But some may wonder, "If a code does exist, how can we be sure it has not been corrupted through time?"

Because of the importance, not only of the message of the Torah, but also of its form, to this day the addition or deletion of a single letter, invalidates an entire Torah scroll. This remarkable precision with the "form" of the text was only too obvious when, with the establishment of the State of Israel, scrolls of the five books of Moses have been brought together from many areas, separated not only by thousands of miles, but by thousands of years.

The Israelite community of Yemen had lived in Arabia since the destruction of the Temple, in 586 B.C. Yet the text of the scrolls they brought are identical to those saved from the Holocaust in Europe. The information concealed in the text given to Moses has been transmitted across centuries of time and miles in its purity, by the pains-taking carefulness of the specially trained *sofreim,* or "writers of the book." Thus the information hidden in the numerical value of the letters is still potentially available. The search reveals marvelous things, and opens a whole new world of understanding of the work of creation. A story that is in remarkable harmony with the latest observations of physicists and cosmologists.

When the United States of America successfully placed the first man on the surface of the Moon, the message that was sent back to Earth was: *"In the beginning God created the heaven and the earth."*

Soon after, a postage stamp was issued, showing a view of the Earth as seen from the Moon. Beside that famous photo were the words, *"In the beginning God."* By the gematria of the Torah, the letter-numbers add to 999.

The number 9 represents wholeness. Raising it to its triplet represents the ultimate manifestation of the wholeness of God (Elohim).

This ultimate manifestation was the creation of *"the heaven and the earth."* The three 9s are planted in that creation.

Diameter of the Sun   864,000 miles (8+6+4=18; 1+8=9)
Diameter of the Earth   7,920 miles (7+9+2=18; 1+8=9)
Diameter of the Moon   2,160 miles (2+1+6=9)
$$9 + 9 + 9 = 27$$

The number 9 is a constant that is built into the fabric of the Universe. It is the number of the mass of an electron, written as m_e – an intrinsic part of the building blocks of creation. One electron has a mass of slightly over 9×10^{-28} of a gram. If this were written out there would be 27 zeros between the decimal and the 9. (.0000000000000000000000000009) The number 9 reveals its meaning by its use in the gematria of the Hebrew and Greek scriptures.

9   *To cause (to bring forth)* בוא
90   *Perfection (wholeness)* כליל
909   *The beginning (creation)* αρχης (II Pet. 3:4)
99   *The garden of the Lord (Eden)* כגן יהוה (Gen. 13:10)
999   *In the beginning God (Elohim)*
        בראשית אלהימ (Genesis 1:1)
999   *I am the root* (Jesus, referring to his position with the Father as part of the Elohim in the work of creation)
εγω ειμι η ριζα (Rev. 22:11)

Many peoples in ancient times thought the Sun was God. Sun worship has been practiced by man throughout all the Earth. And for good reason. It has been obvious to man that the Sun is the source of life, light and heat. It is the biggest and brightest thing up there–indeed a fitting symbol of the true God. And like the true God, the Sun continually gives forth from itself without being diminished.

The seemingly solid Sun is actually a ball of gaseous plasma composed chiefly of hydrogen.

Since hydrogen is the lightest of the elements, it has only one proton in its nucleus, which is orbited by one electron. Thus its atomic number is 1. It aptly represents God, whose identifying number is 1. This is clearly shown in the gematria of both the Hebrew and Greek scriptures.

1000   *Lord,* κυριου

100   *Jehovah has founded,* יהוה יסד (Isa. 14:32)

100   *The Most High,* צל

100   *A great God is Jehovah,* אל גדול יהוה (Psalm 95:3)

One is Unity; and Unity creates by dividing itself. Even the word חצב which means *to divide,* bears the number 100. It is characteristic of God. The prophet Zechariah said *"His name will be called One."* He used the Hebrew word אחד which means *Unity.*

Two is not the result of putting two ones together; for one, by definition, is Unity; therefore all inclusive. Unity, as a symbol of the Creator, divides itself from within, creating a multiplicity. Creation came from within the Creator. It was not the adding of ones to make many. It was the dividing of Unity.

Pythagoras taught his students that 1 is not a number, but the principle of Unity, out of which all numbers emerge. One is immutable and never departs from its own nature, thus $1 \times 1 = 1$ or $1 \div 1 = 1$.

THE FORMULA FOR CREATION

Unity is shown by the hydrogen atom with its characteristic number 1. According to the United States Bureau of Standards, the physical constant (fine structure constant) of the hydrogen atom is $37 \div 27 \times 100$. When we work the problem, it produces two numbers that represent Elohim (the Father and the Son), the first division of Unity–1 and 37.

$$37 \div 27 = 1.370370370 \text{ to infinity}$$

We have found the number 27 to be planted in the Solar System. The numbers 27 and 37 are reciprocals of each other.

$$1 \div 37 = .027027027027 \text{ to infinity}$$
$$1 \div 27 = .037037037037 \text{ to infinity}$$

And look at what happens when we multiply 27×37! We get 999, *"In the beginning God."*

These two numbers, 27 and 37 are basic to the components of creation. Albert Einstein's formula, $E=mc^2$, which is the formula for the obtaining of energy, can be converted to $m=E \div c^2$, which is the formula for obtaining mass (matter). This tells us that matter is created when energy is divided by the speed of light squared. Where does the initial energy and light come from? There is no other source. *"God is power,"* and *"God is light."* The Hebrew word יגיד, which means *to illuminate,* adds to 27. The Hebrew word אור, which means *light,* adds to 207, which, by the rules of gematria is the same as 27, because zeros are merely place holders and add nothing to the number.

Einstein's formula requires the squaring of the speed of light–a seemingly impossible task because the speed of light cannot be exceeded. However, it can be done mathematically. And when we square it, the results are amazing. For our purposes here we will drop the zeros (186,000 miles per second) and multiply 186 x 186 = 34,596. Then resolve the number by adding the digits: $3 + 4 + 5 + 9 + 6 = 27$. Thus the number 27, which we have already found to represent light, becomes the number that also represents c^2.

What is the value of E (energy) in the formula? In the Hebrew text of the Old Testament, God's *great power* is described by the word אול –it has a numerical value of 37. We know that both the light (c^2) and the energy (E) for the formula originated within the Creator himself; and the Hebrew scriptures give us these two basic numbers, 27 and 37, to describe them. Now we can work the formula.

$$m = E \div c^2$$
$$E = 37$$
$$c^2 = 27$$
$$m = 37 \div 27$$
$$m = 1.370370370370 \text{ to infinity}$$

Amazing! Mass (m) is the same number as the physical constant of the hydrogen atom! The formula becomes the basic process of creation–its very source and substance. The Creator's raw materials were energy and light, and they both came from within.

The two numbers, 27 and 37, are basic to creation. The first verse of Genesis reads, *"In the beginning God created the heaven and the earth."* The Hebrew letter-numbers add to 2701. Why is the 1 added? The number 1, as we have seen, represents the Creator. If we divide 2701 by *light* (27), the result is 100.037037037 to infinity. Thus, whereas we had *light* (27), plus the *Creator* (1), now we have *power* (37) plus the *Creator* (1).

The number 37 is used throughout the Hebrew and Greek scriptures to represent the *Elohim* (Father and Son). It is a prime, and is the basis, or foundation for nearly all of the names, titles, and phrases describing the *Elohim*. In *Stonehenge and the Great Pyramid[1]* I list 185 of these names and titles, which add to 37 or multiples of 37. Rather than list them here, I have included them in Appendix I.

The number 37 is a prime–that is, it is only divisible by 1. However, when each of the 9 digits is raised to its triplet, they are all divisible by 37, in increments of 3, thus:

$1 \times 37 = 37$ *God,* אלהא

$3 \times 37 = 111$ *The Most High,* עליא

$6 \times 37 = 222$ *I am Alpha and Omega,*
$\qquad \varepsilon\gamma\omega\ A\lambda\phi\alpha\ \kappa\alpha\iota\ \Omega\mu\varepsilon\gamma\alpha$

$9 \times 37 = 333$ *Lord of Lords,* $K\upsilon\rho\iota\sigma\varsigma\ \tau\omega\nu\ \kappa\upsilon\rho\iota\omega\nu$

$12 \times 37 = 444$ *The Lord Christ,* $\tau\omega\ K\upsilon\rho\iota\omega\ X\rho\iota\sigma\tau\omega$

$15 \times 37 = 555$ *Our Lord and His Christ,*
$\qquad K\upsilon\rho\iota\upsilon\ \eta\mu\omega\nu\ \kappa\alpha\iota\ \tau\upsilon\ X\rho\iota\sigma\tau\upsilon\ \alpha\upsilon\tau\upsilon$

$18 \times 37 = 666$ *Jehovah that created the heavens*
$\qquad$ האל יהוה בורא השמים

$21 \times 37 = 777$ *The Man Child,* $\tau\sigma\nu\ \alpha\rho\sigma\varepsilon\nu\alpha$

$24 \times 37 = 888$ *Jesus,* $I\eta\sigma\sigma\upsilon\varsigma$

$+\ 27 \times 37 = 999$ *Glory of God,* $\delta\sigma\xi\alpha\nu\ \Theta\varepsilon\omega$

$\overline{136} = $ *I am Jehovah, the first and last,* (Isaiah 41:4)
$\qquad$ אני יהוה ראשון ואת אחרנים

---

1 Bonnie Gaunt, *Stonehenge and the Great Pyramid: Window on the Universe,* 1993, pp. 121-133. (Order from Bonnie Gaunt, 510 Golf Avenue, Jackson, MI 49203 (U.S.A.), $10.00)

In chapter 1 we saw that the circle which represents *El,* or Unity, divides and projects an exact image of itself outward, producing the two overlapping circles precisely pictured by the hydrogen molecule.

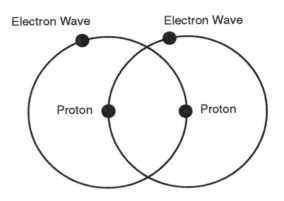

These two overlapping circles produce a third figure which is common to both. It is known as the Vesica. In Colossians 1:15 we are told that the Son *"is the image of the invisible God, the firstborn of every creature."* The Vesica that is formed by this "growth by division" was used by early Christians as the symbol of Christ–the fish. The sign of the fish is still used by Christians today. But it was not an invention of the Christian era. The Hebrew word *fish,* דאג, in the Old Testament, has the number equivalent of 8–the number that represents Jesus, *(Ιησους = 888),* and more specifically a new beginning through Him, *(beginning,* אז = 8). But the Hebrew word כדגי, which, when translated into English means *"like a fish,"* has a number equivalent of 37. It was not a chance coincidence. It was part of a magnificent code, built into all creation, by a Master Mathematician, the Creator!

The hydrogen molecule consists of two protons surrounded by the wave bubbles of two electrons, with their characteristic number 9. The two wave bubbles pass through each other and become a bonded unit. Thus the two characteristic 9s become 18 – the basic number that always relates to the Creator. This number will be shown later in its beauty, but for now, let's take a closer look at the hydrogen molecule.

The electrons have a negative charge, while the two protons are positively charged. The electrons maintain a respectable distance from the protons, forming a ball of negative charge around each proton, like little bubbles of wave energy. In any heavier atom, this balance could not be maintained without neutrons to give it stability–to keep it from blowing apart. The hydrogen atom, however, needs no neutrons for its stability; it is self contained.

The wave bubbles surrounding the two protons overlap and pass through each other like ripples on a pond, each maintaining its own pattern, without destroying the pattern of the other. Each nucleus gets its part share in the two electrons.

This principle illustrates *El* becoming *Elohim* as discussed in chapter 1. It is growth by division. The second becomes the image of the first, just as the Son became the exact image of the Father. The principle is active at the cellular level. This process of growth by division is called *mitosis*.

When two bubbles of the same substance are joined, the same pattern will always appear. They conform to a fixed law. The tiny electron bubbles of the hydrogen molecule are, of course, too small for us to see; however, the identical same laws apply to soap bubbles which we can see.

How well I remember blowing soap bubbles, as a child,

and watching their fluid colors float on the moving air. But occasionally two bubbles will collide. Then an interesting phenomenon takes place. The two bubbles will immediately join in a configuration exactly like the two electron bubbles in the hydrogen molecule; however, they do not pass through each other, but interface with a flat side shared by both. If we were to project the circles, the outer edge of each bubble would reach precisely to the center of its partner. It will always do this. It is a law of physics. This exact pattern results from the first division of the fertilized human egg cell.

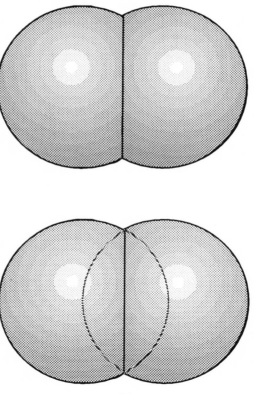

THE FORMULA FOR CREATION

The number 37 is unmistakably the number of the Elohim (see Appendix I). Let's assign this number to the width of the Vesica Piscis (the vessel of the fish).

37 *Like a fish,* כדגי

The diameter of each circle would become 74, the number that describes the beginning of creation.

74 *Creation,* κτισις
740 *Foundation,* יסד
740 *Circle,* κυκλος
74 *Everlasting,* עד

The Vesica formed by the two overlapping circles has a height of 64 and a width of 37. Subtract, and the difference between height and width is 27, the number basic to creation. Multiply 64 x 37 and the product is 2,368 – the number value of *Jesus Christ, Ιησους Χριστος.*

64 x 37 = 2,368
Jesus Christ = 2,368

The number 64 is the letter-number value of *Truth,* αληθεια. Jesus was the personification of Truth. In fact, he said, *"I am the Truth."*

The proportional dimensions of the cross can be inscribed within the Vesica. It would have a height of 64 and a cross beam of 29.6. The *Only Begotten,* μονογενη, has a number equivalent of 296, as does *Son of Man, υιος του ανθρωπου,* 2960. It was the only begotten of the Father who hung upon that cross, in a human body, a son of man. I do not think it coincidence that 8 *(fish,* דאג*),* times 296 produces 2,368, the letter-number equivalent for Jesus Christ.

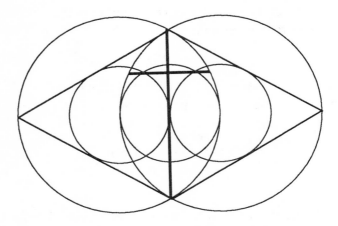

The proportion of the cross becomes 80 to 37. The numbers 8 and 37 profoundly represent the man Christ Jesus who hung upon that cross.

$$8 \times 37 = 296$$
Only begotten = 296
Son of Man = 2,960

The hydrogen molecule, representing the Elohim, when placed within a box, shows the wholeness of the unit–division of Unity, retaining its wholeness.

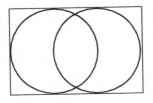

37 Width of Vesica
370 Perimeter box
370 *Whole, ολος*
370 *Whole, שלם*

THE FORMULA FOR CREATION

Based on the width of the Vesica being represented by the number 37, the perimeter of the box will be 370. As if to confirm the meaning of the number, both the Hebrew and the Greek scriptures define it by the word *whole*.

370 *Whole,* ολος
370 *Whole,* שלם

Albert Einstein, as a young man, had a quest for knowledge. His work of a lifetime was the unfolding of the heart of knowledge, like the opening of a simple, yet beautiful flower, petal by petal. His discoveries forced the revision of all fundamental thinking about time and space.

Einstein's response to nature was that of being in the presence of something God-like.

An article in Time magazine (December 28, 1992) referring to atheism as a denial of the existence of God, posed the question: "If you admit that we can't peer behind the curtain, how can you be sure there's nothing there?"[1]

We can, in fact, peer behind the curtain; and what we find is beautiful beyond all human imagination, and in perfect harmony with the laws of physics. We find the ultimate origins of matter and energy; and we do indeed find God.

The two electrons of the hydrogen molecule, with their characteristic number 9, when added, become 18 – the number that represents the Creator . The biblical term for the Creator is *Maker,* פעל, and its letter-numbers add to 180.

The hydrogen atom, which so beautifully represents God, has the atomic weight of 1.0080 – the lightest of the elements. These two numerals, 1 and 8 represent the *beginning* (1), and

---

1 Used by permission of Time, Inc.

a *new beginning* (8) through Jesus Christ. Below is a sample of how 18 is used in the gematria of the Hebrew and Greek scriptures.

180   *Maker* (the Creator, פעל

18   *He who lives* (Jehovah), חי

1800 *I am the living One*, εγω ειμι ο ζων, (Rev. 1:17-18)

1008 *The work of thy fingers* (creation),

         מעשה אצבעתיך, (Psalm 8:3)

1080 *God himself that formed the Earth and made it*,

         הוא האלהים יצר הארץ ועשה, (Isaiah 45:18)

108   *Two parts* (to divide in half), חצי

1080 *Heaven is my throne and the Earth is my footstool*,

         השמים כסאי והארץ הדם רגלי, (Isaiah 66:1)

1080 *The Lord is in his holy temple, let all the Earth keep*

     silence before him, יהוה בהיכל קדשו הם מפניו כל הארץ

     (Hab. 2:20)

1008 *The Lord is high above all the nations, and his glory*

     above the heavens, רם על כל גוים יהוה על השמים כבודו

     (Psalm 113:4)

The number 1 represents *God,* the Beginner, and the number 8 represents *Jesus* (888), the New Beginner. The *Holy Spirit*, πνευμα το αγιον, also bears the number 1,080. If we multiply 1,080 by 8 the product is the solar number 8,640. The Sun, a ball of hydrogen, represents the One, the 1, the Beginning!

The Earth has a diameter of 7,920 miles, and its satellite and companion, the Moon, has a diameter of 2,160 miles (radius 1,080 miles). The combined diameters of this unit are 10,080 miles.

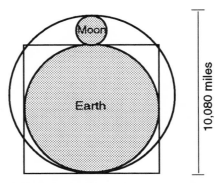

Atomic weight of the hydrogen atom, 1.0080
Combined diameters of Earth and Moon, 10,080 miles

It was not a chance coincidence. It was part of a master design–a design that was to include man.

Elohim said, "Let us make man in our image, after our likeness." (Genesis 1:26)

Man was indeed made in the *image* and *likeness* of his Creator. He bore the same numbers and the same proportions. The Earth was made for man–and man for the earth.

...God himself who formed the Earth and made it; he hath established it. He created it not in vain, he formed it to be inhabited. (Isaiah 45:18)

This relationship of man to his Earth was shown by the centuries-old drawing by the Italian artist, Leonardo daVinci. He showed that man's outstretched arms define a square, and his raised arms and extended legs define a circle–the identical proportions of Earth and Moon.

59

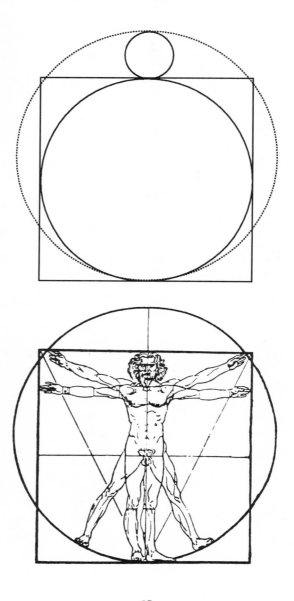

THE FORMULA FOR CREATION

The center of the square is the sex organ–that which enables man to reproduce, to pro-create. The center of the circle is the navel–that which joins the infant to its mother, its lifeline. The circle, representing the Creator, and the square representing that which was created, are centered in dependence upon the Creator for life (navel) and passing that life on (sex organ). The relationship is profound! It is far more than coincidence. It is communication! It is telling us that there is a master design, produced by a Master Designer.

Human reproduction, like all biological reproduction is, at the cellular level, growth by division–*mitosis.*

This principle for self-replication, involving the genetic code of DNA, permits the continuation of initial life, in an orderly and renewable process.

DNA (deoxyribonucleic acid) is the chemical constituent of the genes of an organism. All the information for the structure of that organism is contained in the sequence of building blocks in the DNA chain. This chain resembles a double helix, like a twisted ladder. The two posts of the ladder are sugar-phosphate strands. These are paired together by means of hydrogen bonds, which form the rungs of the ladder.

A right handed helix completes one turn for every 10 rungs of the ladder; and a left handed helix completes one turn for every 12 rungs of the ladder. The pattern is always consistent and predictable. The bonding together by means of hydrogen is the inseparable link between the created and the Creator. The numbers themselves are basic to the number code found in all creation.

A student of the Bible soon realizes that the number 12 is basic to its number code. There are so many 12s mentioned in scripture that it cannot be overlooked. It is a "foundation" number. In fact there are two basic words in the Hebrew scriptures that are translated *foundation:* מוסדי = 120, and יסד = 74. Look at what happens when we add or multiply these two foundation numbers.

$12 + 74 = 86$ *Elohim,* אלהים
$12 \times 74 = 888$ *Jesus, Iησους*

The Hebrew word for *one* or *first* is חד and adds to 12. The Greek word for *creation,* as used in the New Testament is κτισις, which adds to 74. They are inseparably joined in the Elohim. They are telling us *"In the beginning Elohim created the heaven and the earth,"* (Genesis 1:1).

We saw that number 6 was basic to the concept of creation in the first word of Genesis–*Breshith*–it being a play on words, using the two Hebrew words *bara* and *shith,* which means *"created six."* I would like to show how 6 and 12 are basic to all life on earth.

The foundation material for all organic substance is glucose–a basic ingredient in DNA. It is made by reactions that combine carbon dioxide (CO_2) and water (H_2O), releasing oxygen into the air. The process can be written like this:

$6\,CO_2$	$+$	$6\,H_2O$	$=$	$C_6H_{12}O_6$	$+$	$6\,O_2$
6 carbon dioxide	+	6 water	=	glucose	+	6 oxygen molecules or 12 oxygen atoms

THE FORMULA FOR CREATION

The reaction that makes this molecular conversion, which is basic to all organic life, requires energy from an outside source. This energy need is met by light from the Sun. Light energy is absorbed by the green pigment in plants, called chlorophyll. The chlorophyll then uses this energy to pull the oxygen away from the two hydrogen atoms in a molecule of water. The two oxygen atoms then combine to make a molecule of oxygen, which flies free in the air. The process is called, *photosynthesis,* from the Greek words *photos,* meaning *light,* and *synthesis,* meaning *putting together.*

All life on Earth, both plant and animal, is made possible by this light-sensitive substance called chlorophyll, which is characterized by the numbers 6 and 12.

Chlorophyll seems almost to be a magic substance. In short, it converts energy into matter by means of light. It gets back to the basic concept of $m = E \div c^2$ – it takes energy and light to make matter.

What is this "magic" substance? Strangely it is almost identical to hematin, which is one of the compounds in human blood–an essential for life. The structure of the chlorophyll molecule is a ring with a single magnesium atom at its center. The magnesium atom has 12 protons in its nucleus, therefore it carries the atomic number of 12. Hematin is a similar ring with a single atom of iron at its center. The iron atom has 26 protons in its nucleus, thus it bears the atomic number of 26. The significance of these two numbers does not go unnoticed. 12 is the foundation number, and 26 is the gematria (by addition) of the tetragrammaton, the unpronounceable name, *Jehovah.*

The chlorophyll molecule unfolds into a pattern of 6 circles, divided into increments of 30°, making 12 branches.

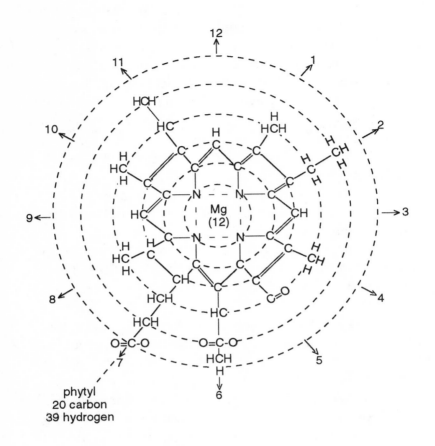

phytyl
20 carbon
39 hydrogen

Chlorophyll Molecule
6 circles
12 branches
Total of 137 atoms

THE FORMULA FOR CREATION

Chlorophyll Molecule

	Atoms	Protons
Center	1 Magnesium x 12	12
Circle 1	4 Nitrogen x 7	28
Circle 2	8 Carbon x 6	48
Circle 3	12 Carbon x 6 5 Hydrogen x 1	72 } 5 } 77
Circle 4	9 Carbon x 6 18 Hydrogen x 1 1 Oxygen x 8	54 18 } 80 8
Circle 5	4 Carbon x 6 2 Oxygen x 8 7 Hydrogen x 1	24 16 } 47 7
Circle 6	2 Carbon x 6 2 Oxygen x 8 3 Hydrogen x 1	12 16 } 31 3
Phytyl	20 Carbon x 6 39 Hydrogen x 1	120 } 39 } 159
	137	482

The total number of atoms in the chlorophyll molecule is 137. We are back to basics again. The formula for creation, $m = E \div c^2$, told us that m=1.370370370 – the 1 and the 37 being the numbers for Elohim, the Creator. The number 137 is also the addition of the letter-numbers in אלהי האלהים, *The God of gods.*

The total number of protons in the chlorophyll molecule is 482. The letter-numbers אלהי ישענו, *The God of our salvation,* add to 482. Read the numbers from right to left, as in Hebrew, and it is 284, which is the addition of the letter-numbers for *God (Theos), Θεος.*

This pattern of 6 and 12 is shown again in the process of photosynthesis. Light from the Sun shining on the chlorophyll in plants, converts water and carbon dioxide into organic matter. With the energy provided by sunlight, the chlorophyll takes 6 molecules of water and 6 molecules of carbon dioxide, breaks them down into their separate atoms, and transfers the hydrogen atoms from the water to the carbon dioxide. In the process, 12 of the oxygen atoms are left over, and are released into the air.

The new molecule thus formed is glucose, having 6 atoms of carbon, 12 atoms of hydrogen, and 6 atoms of oxygen ($C_6H_{12}O_6$). It can be simply illustrated by the diagram below. This primary process of all life on Earth uses the basic numbers of 6 and 12.

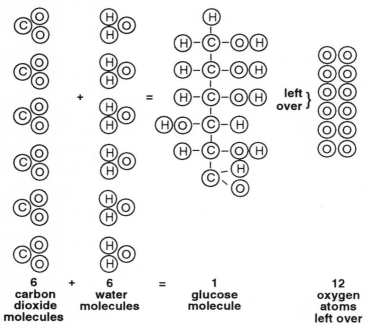

6	+	6	=	1		12
carbon		water		glucose		oxygen
dioxide		molecules		molecule		atoms
molecules						left over

THE FORMULA FOR CREATION

Photosynthesis

6 molecules of carbon dioxide combine with 6 molecules of water to produce one molecule of glucose.

6 molecules of carbon dioxide:

carbon:	6 protons x 6	=	36
oxygen:	8 protons x 12	=	96
			132

6 molecules of water:

hydrogen:	1 proton x 12	=	12
oxygen:	8 protons x 6	=	48
			60

Total number of protons   192

Makes 1 molecule of glucose:

hydrogen:	1 proton x 12	=	12
carbon:	6 protons x 6	=	36
oxygen:	8 protons x 6	=	48
Total number of protons			96

12 atoms of oxygen given off:

oxygen:	8 protons x 12	=	96

The numbers are profound! They are 132, 60, 192 and 96. These magnificent numbers, involved in the basis of all life on earth, are used in the gematria of the Hebrew and Greek scriptures thus:

132   *Jehovah your God,* יהוה אלהיכם (Josh. 4:5)

132   *A God of gods,* אלה אלהין (Dan. 2:47)

60   *Jehovah the Redeemer,* יהוה גאל (Isa. 49:7)

192   *The Lord of Glory,* τον κυριον της δοξης (I Cor. 2:8)

192   *The everlasting God,* אלהי עולם (Isa. 40:28)

192   *The Lord Most High,* יהוה עליון (Psalm 47:2)

96   *The God of all,* אלהי כל

BEGINNINGS

The conversion of light into organic substance is based in the number 6. The process begins with 6 molecules of water and 6 molecules of carbon dioxide.

Some have suggested that 6 is a sinister number, and represents that which is evil. Its primary use in the gematria of the Old and New Testaments tells a story that is just the opposite. (I say "primary use," because there appears to be a law, that the numbers of the sacred code also have an opposite and less used meaning from their primary meaning.) In fact, the Hebrew word that means *righteousness,* or *uprightness,* מישרים, adds to 600. The Hebrew title for the Creator, *Elohim,* אלהים, multiplies to 6 (dropping the zeros). *World, cosmos,* in Greek, $\kappa o\sigma\mu o\varsigma$, adds to 600. *Light,* מחזה, adds to 60. It becomes apparent that the basics of creation bear the number 6. Raising the number 6 to its triplet, its ultimate concept, we find 666 to be the addition of the letter-numbers of *"Jehovah God that created the heavens,"* (Isaiah 42:5); or, 666 is the addition of the letter-numbers for *"He hath made the earth,"* (Jeremiah 10:12). And 666 is the addition of the letter-numbers for *"Let there be lights,"* (Genesis 1:14).[1]

600	*Righteousness,* מישרים
600	*Elohim,* אלהים (by multiplication)
600	*World, cosmos,* $\kappa o\sigma\mu o\varsigma$
666	*Jehovah God that created the heavens,*
	האל יהוה בורא השמים, (Isaiah 42:5)

---

1 The number 666 is used by the Antichrist in Revelation 13:18. He is an imposter. He not only usurps the name and position of Christ, he also usurps the number 666. *"And his number is six hundred threescore and six,"* adds to 2,368, which is the number for *Jesus Christ, $I\eta\sigma o\upsilon\varsigma\ X\rho\iota\sigma\tau o\varsigma$.* The one is the imposter of the other, and counterfeits the number.

THE FORMULA FOR CREATION

666   *He hath made the earth,* ארץ עשה, (Jer. 10:12)

666   *Let there by lights,* מארת יהי, (Genesis 1:14)

666   *Excellency,* יתרון

The creation of all life on Earth starts with the energy obtained from light. The Hebrew word for light, אור, when multiplied, produces 12. Light from the Sun represents the life force, or energy, from the Creator. The Hebrew word for *Almighty,* שדי, multiplies to 12. The Hebrew words for *The Living God,* חיא אלהא, multiply to 12. It is no coincidence, nor is it anything contrived by man. It is a basic part of the relationship of the Creator to all life on Earth!

Light, then, appears to be the link between the Creator and all living substance.

5
Let There Be Light

Genesis 1:3 gives us the first recorded words of the Creator.

God said, "Let there be light," and there was light.

Light–the link between the Creator and all living substance–is the beginning of Creation. It is basic and essential to all the remaining acts of creation.

The formula for creation, $m=E\div c^2$, has shown us that all matter (m) is the result of energy (E) divided by the speed of light squared (c^2). The numbers that were substituted for the symbols led us to the fine structure constant of the hydrogen atom. I have attempted to show the relationship between the hydrogen atom and the *El;* and the extension of the concept to the relationship between the hydrogen molecule and the *Elohim.* Hydrogen, the lightest element, and the first one, is thus linked with the Creator and the first act of creation.

The Sun, our primary source of light on Earth, is a ball of gaseous plasma composed mostly of hydrogen. The weight of its mass, under the pull of its own gravity, raises its internal temperature to 15 million °C. This extreme heat causes the fusion of the hydrogen, forming helium. In the process, a small amount of the mass in each hydrogen nucleus is converted into pure energy ($E=mc^2$). It is this energy that lights and heats our Solar System, and is the reason that life can exist on Earth.

If one hydrogen atom could be totally converted into energy, it would equal 10^{15} GeV. (GeV means a billion electron volts.) For purposes of comparison, the energy released when we burn something is about one electron volt. The energy potential in one hydrogen atom, 10^{15} GeV, is incomprehensible to human awareness. It is 1 followed by 15 zeros, multiplied by one billion.

Although it is more than our minds can handle, let's look at that recurring number 15. We can handle that.

The internal temperature of the Sun is 15 million °C. And the energy in just one hydrogen atom is 10^{15} GeV. Thus our source of light is characterized by the number 15. Is it any surprise that the Greek word for *light, φως,* as used throughout the New Testament, has the number equivalent of 1500. This word, *φως,* is pronounced *phos,* and is the basis of our common word *photo* which we still use to identify light.

The speed that light travels to us from the Sun is 186,000 miles per second. Today's physics has refined that figure to 186,282. However, the rounded figure of 186,000 is generally used, and for our purposes, certainly is the number that *represents* the speed of light.

It takes light from the Sun 8.33333 minutes to reach the Earth. The reciprocal of 12 is .0833333. As we saw in the previous chapter, photosynthesis, the conversion of light into matter is built upon 6 and 12. The reciprocal of 15 *(light)* is .066666.

When the letter-numbers for *light* in Hebrew are multiplied, they produce 12 (אור, 200 x 6 x 1 = 12, dropping the zeros). Add the definite article, and *the light* multiplies to 6 (האור, 200 x 6 x 1 x 5 = 6, dropping the zeros). These numbers, 6 and 12 are the very basis of the conversion of light into matter, in the process of photosynthesis.

Perhaps the 6 divisions of the works of creation were part of the basic pattern of creation, rather than a time measurement.

Let's look again at these numbers for light and creation, 15 and 6 and 12. They are basic, and they are beautiful.

The tetragrammaton, the unpronounceable name of the Creator, יהוה, bears the letter-numbers 10, 5, 6, and 5, reading from right to left. Adding them gives us 26. Multiplying them gives 1,500, and the squares of the numbers give us 186.

26   *Light,* נהרה or ניר or קלקל (added)

26   *Jehovah,* יהוה (added)

1500   *Light,* φως, (added)

1500   *Jehovah,* יהוה (multiplied)

186,000   Speed of light

186   *Jehovah* (squared), י² ה ²ו ²ה ²י

The interplay between the numbers for the Creator and the basic numbers of light and creation is amazing. It is not just a coincidence that:

6   *Elohim,* אלהים (multiplied)

6   *Let there be light,* יהי אור (multiplied)

12   *The living God,* אלהא חיא (multiplied)

12   *Light,* אור (multiplied)

15   *Jehovah* (1500), יהוה (multiplied)

15   *Light* (1500), φως (added)

72

The other Hebrew words for *God* also multiply to 15.

$$אלה \ = \ 15$$
$$אלהא \ = \ 15$$
$$אלהי \ = \ 15$$

The Greek word for *beginning, γενεσις (genesis),* also multiplies to 15. It is the Greek word used to name the first book of the Bible, describing the beginning. Its connection to light, both in word and in number is unmistakable.

In chapter 4 I suggested the formula for creation to be m=37÷27. Just for a moment, let's substitute other numbers for *power* and *light* in the formula. If m (matter) equals E (energy) divided by c^2 (speed of light squared), then what would happen if we substituted 1,500 for both *light* and *power.* The reason for doing this is because 1,500 is the gematria for both of those words in Greek, by addition.

1500   *Light, φως*
1500   *Power, δυναμεως*

$m \ = \ E \div c^2$
$m \ = \ 1{,}500 \div 1{,}500^2$
$m \ = \ 1{,}500 \div 2{,}250{,}000$
$m \ = \ .00066666$
(It is the same as the reciprocal
of *light,* $1 \div 1{,}500 = .00066666$)

In the formula for creation, matter is represented by 6, the basic number in the conversion of light into matter by photosynthesis–the first perfect number and the only number that is both the sum and the product of its factors. Thus 1+2+3=6 and 1x2x3=6. When God said, *"Let there be lights,"*

(Sun and Moon), he was giving the ultimate manifestation of the meaning of 6, for the command, in Hebrew, is יהי מארת, and it adds to 666.

The number 6 (and its double, 12) is basic to the transformation of light into all living substance. It is the fundamental number of creation. The key that unlocks the number 6 is, in fact, the Hebrew word for *key*, מפתח, which adds to 528, and its Greek equivalent, $\kappa\lambda\epsilon\iota\delta\alpha$, multiplies to 12. (The number 528 is familiar to all, for there are 5,280 feet in one British mile.) A key is that which either locks or unlocks. When we find the key to something, we immediately think that it will unlock that something. How does 528 unlock the meaning of 6? One way is by multiplication. Multiply 6 x 528 and the product is 3,168, the number equivalent for *Lord Jesus Christ, $K\upsilon\rho\iota\circ\varsigma$ $I\eta\sigma\circ\upsilon\varsigma$ $X\rho\iota\sigma\tau\circ\varsigma$.* As part of the Elohim, he was the agent through whom all creation was accomplished.

All things were made by Him, and without Him
was not anything made that was made. (John 1:3)

Let's apply the *"key"* to light. The above text of scripture goes on to say that He was the *"true light."* As we have seen, the characteristic number for light is 15. Light is the necessary ingredient for the creation of all organic substance on Earth, through the process of photosynthesis. Therefore, let's use the *key* to unlock 15. When we multiply 15 by the *key*, 528, the product is 7,920–the Earth number (Earth's mean diameter). The Earth is the only place in our Solar System, and possibly in the Universe, where organic substance is created through photosynthesis.

The language of numbers is a beautiful language. It was the language of the Creator. He spoke and worlds were made.

LET THERE BE LIGHT

By the word of the Lord were the heavens made;
and all the host of them by the breath of his mouth.
(Psalm 33:6)

The Sun, which is a beautiful symbol of the Creator, has a diameter of 864,000 miles. Its relationship to that Creator through the language of number is profound. One of the Greek words for God is *Θεων,* and it adds to 864. A description of Him is given in Hebrews 12:29–*"God is fire."* In Greek it is *Θεος πυρ,* and it adds to 864. Even the word *holy, αγιων,* which describes Him, adds to 864. That same God, the Beginner, spoke through the prophet Isaiah, *"Before Me there was no God formed, neither shall there be after me,"* (Isaiah 43:10). The Hebrew words were לפני לא נצר אל ואחרי לא יהיה, and they add to 864. The symbol is obvious–the brightness of the Sun is necessary for life to exist on Earth.

That brightness travels a distance of 93 million miles to reach us, and warm the Earth with its life-giving rays. The *brightness* of the Sun was spoken of by the Apostle Paul, and he used a Greek word for *brightness, λαμπροτητα,* which adds to 930, (Acts 26:13). The impact of the symbol can best be appreciated by a simple diagram.

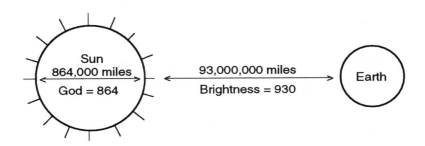

75

93,000,000 miles converted to inches, and divided by the speed of light, gives 3,168–the number value for *Lord Jesus Christ*. That brightness engulfs the Earth as it rotates on its axis, and in one period of 24 hours, the whole Earth will be bathed in its light. 93,000,000 miles converted to inches, divided by the mean circumference of the Earth (its surface), gives 2,368–the number value of *Jesus Christ*.

The relationship of the Sun to the Son can be shown by their number values.

53   *Sun,* חמה

53   *Son,* υιον (530)

86   *Elohim,* אלהים

+ 232   *Let there be light,* יהי אור

318   *Sun,* ηλιος

318 x π = 999   *In the beginning Elohim*

בראשית אלהים (Genesis 1:1)

Such number relationships are not likely to be random chance. They reveal the hand of a Master Designer.

The brightness that comes from the Sun we call sunshine. Sunshine is spoken of in the Old Testament, using the Hebrew words יזרח שמש, which, by the rules of gematria, give 864. Even more startling are the two words in Greek:

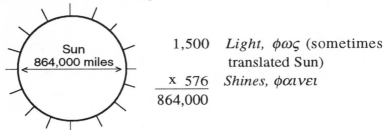

1,500	*Light,* φως (sometimes translated Sun)
x 576	*Shines,* φαινει
864,000	

LET THERE BE LIGHT

Jesus Christ was said to be the *"true light"* (John 1:19). The two Greek words are φως αληθινον and add to 1,728.

$$2 \times 864 = 1,728$$
$$\textit{True Light} = 1,728$$

Light from the Sun reaches the earth in 8.33333 minutes, at the speed of 11,160,000 miles per minute. If the distance it travels were stated in inches, 589,248 (dropping zeros), and divided by 1,116 (miles per minute, dropping zeros), the result would be 5,280, the *key,* and the number of feet in the British mile.

The true origins of the mile unit are indeed based in the relationship of the Sun to the Earth.

For the purposes of mapping the Earth, men have covered our globe with an imaginary grid. East-west lines are called latitude, or parallels, because they are parallel to each other. North-south lines are called longitude, or meridians. These are farthest apart at the equator and converge at the poles.

Parallels never meet, so the distance between two lines of latitude does not change. One degree of latitude is about 69 miles.

Because meridians do meet, one degree of longitude is shorter near the poles than at the equator. However, 15 degrees of longitude *always* equals the amount of Earth that is bathed in sunlight for one hour, thus each time zone is 15° –a basic number of light. The 15° of longitude, of course, receives its sunlight on its surface, which would be about 1,660 miles along the equator, considering the fact that the Earth bulges at the equator. However, if we measured this path of sunlight on the Earth's mean diameter, it would cover precisely 528 miles in one hour–the number that is used in the British Mile unit–5,280 feet. Thus the true origin of the mile unit is based in light and time.

Light and time. An interesting association. Before there was light there was no time. We set our clock by the light from the Sun. We call it solar time. The multiplying of light by time, gives us the speed of light, not only mathematically, but by gematria as well.

$$
\begin{array}{rl}
1,500 & \text{\textit{Light,} } \phi\omega\varsigma \\
\underline{\times\ 124} & \text{\textit{Time,} עדן} \\
186,000 & \text{(speed of light)}
\end{array}
$$

The distance from the Sun to Earth is 93,000,000 miles. Considering the Earth and Moon as an inseparable unit, together orbiting the Sun, let's observe the distance that light travels to the unit. Combining the diameters of the Earth-Moon unit we get 10,080 miles. Add this to the distance to the Sun. The total will be 93,010,080 miles. Just for fun, let's find the square root of that number, $\sqrt{93,010,080} = 9,644$, then multiply the digits, 9 x 6 x 4 x 4 and the product will be 864, the solar number. An interesting exercise in numbers, but truly profound.

Earth's orbit of the Sun is an ellipse; however, if we doubled the mean distance from Sun to Earth, we would have an approximation of the mean of Earth's orbit. This would be 186,000,000 miles. Convert it to feet and drop the zeros, then divide by 3,168 *(Lord Jesus Christ)*, and the result will be 31, which is the number value (by addition) of *El*–the first.

$$
\begin{array}{l}
186 \ \times \ 528 \ = \ 98,208 \\
98,208 \ \div \ 3,168 \ = \ 31
\end{array}
$$

Or base the computation on Earth's distance from the Sun, 93,000,000 miles. Convert to feet and divide by 3,168 *(Lord Jesus Christ),* and the result will be 155, the *First, πρωτος,* 1,550.

The speed of light, 186 thousand miles per second, is a basic number that relates to the Earth in many ways. The Earth is spoken of in scripture as God's workmanship, or *"His work."* In Deuteronomy 32:4 we find the statement: *"He is the Rock, His work is perfect."* The Hebrew word for *"His work"* is פעלו and adds to 186. It multiplies to 10,080, which is the combined diameters of Earth and Moon. In Isaiah 64:4 the Hebrew word מעולם is used with reference to the beginning of the world. It also adds to 186. Thus it becomes apparent that light and creation are inseparably linked.

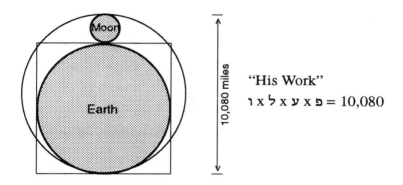

"His Work"
פ x ע x ל x ו = 10,080

Earth's crust, the lithosphere, is composed basically of 12 elements. Their atomic numbers (the number of protons in the nucleus of each) total 186. Thus, the only place where life, as we know it, can exist in our Solar System bears the number of light.

BEGINNINGS

The mean composition of Earth's crust corresponds fairly closely to a mixture of granite and basalt, in equal proportions; these are the most common igneous rocks from which sedimentary and metamorphic rocks have been derived. In these rocks oxygen is absolutely predominant: the crust consists almost entirely of oxygen compounds.

99% of Earth's crust is composed of 12 elements. All the other elements together make up the remaining 1%. These predominant 12 elements, then, are the basic components of this thin rock crust, the lithosphere. They are listed below. Their combined atomic numbers and atomic weights total to numbers that are absolutely startling in their relationship to light and to rock. It appears to be the work of a Master Architect.

	Atomic Number	Atomic Weight
Oxygen	8	16
Silicon	14	28
Aluminum	13	27
Iron	26	56
Calcium	20	40
Sodium	11	23
Potassium	19	39
Magnesium	12	24
Titanium	22	48
Phosphorus	15	31
Hydrogen	1	1
Manganese	25	55
	186	388

LET THERE BE LIGHT

186,000 miles per second – speed of light

186	*Jehovah is my Rock,* סלע יהוה (Psalm 18:2)
186	*Great Rock,* סלע כבד (Isa. 32:1)
186	*His work,* פעלו (Deut. 32:4)
186	*From everlasting* (the beginning of the world) מעולם (Isa. 64:4)
186	*Golgotha* (the rock where Jesus was crucified) Γολγοθα

388	*The Sun,* ο ηλιος
388	*One God,* γαρ Θεος, (I Tim. 2:5)
388	*Rock,* חלמיש

It is quite convincing that the numbers were intentional. The words used in the Old and New Testaments to describe light and its source, the Sun, and Earth's rocks, are in complete agreement with the atomic structure of rocks in our lithosphere. Only an Architect with infinite knowledge could have planned and executed such harmony. The probability of a coincidence is too remote to calculate.

In the Old Testament, the book of Job contains some profound statements regarding the beginning of things. God asked Job:

> *Where wast thou when I laid the foundations of the Earth? Declare if thou hast understanding. Who laid the measures thereof, if thou knowest? Or who hath stretched the measuring line upon it? Upon what are her foundation-pillars made to sink? Or who laid the cornerstone?* (Job 38:4-6)

The bedrock of these foundation-pillars, Earth's crust, bears the number 186, the number that identifies light. They were four, thus 4 x 186 = 744. Representing the circle of the Earth, this would produce a diameter of 2,368 – the number value of *Jesus Christ, Ιησους Χριστος.*

The *"two great lights"* spoken of in Genesis 1, (the Sun and Moon), have a number value of 744 – המאורת הגדלים.

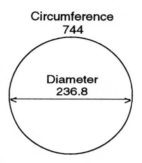

Circumference
744

Diameter
236.8

If Earth's mean distance from the Sun were stated in inches and divided by the diameter of the Earth, the result would be 744 – the gematria for *two great lights.*

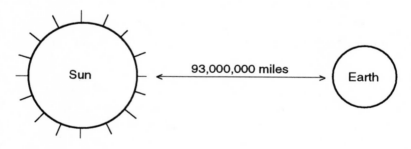

Sun

93,000,000 miles

Earth

93 x 6,336 = 589,248 (dropping zeros)
589,248 ÷ 7,920 = 74.4 – *Two great lights,* המאורת הגדלים
7 + 4 + 4 = 15 – *Light,* $\phi\omega\varsigma$ = 1,500

LET THERE BE LIGHT

The Apostle John said that Jesus Christ was *the light* that was sent into the world. The title bears the number 2640. This number, multiplied by the foundation number, 12 (the *key* multiplied), produces 3,168, the number for *Lord Jesus Christ, Κυριος Ιησους Χριστος.*

> 2640   *The Light*
> 264 x 12 = 3,168
> 3,168   *Lord Jesus Christ*

Yes, the *two great lights* were to be not only for seasons and for days and years, they were to be for *signs!* Signs of what? Signs of the *truth* of the existence of God.

>   264   *Signs, σημεια*
>   264   *Truth, αληθειας*
> + 264   *The Light, του φωτος* (2640)
>   792   (the number that represents Earth)

Truth, 264, multiplied by the *key,* 528, produces 139,392, which is the number of yards in the mean diameter of the Earth (1,393,920).

The ancient Hebrew prophet, Hosea, describing the Creator, said, *"His going forth is prepared as the morning,"* (Hos. 6:3) The metaphor *"as the morning"* is the Hebrew word כשחר, which adds to 528. It has reference to *the breaking forth of light.* The number 528 is the *key* that unlocks the power of *light,* and brings life to Earth.

In 1666, Isaac Newton conducted an experiment, passing a beam of white light through a three-sided piece of glass, a prism. The light that came out on the other side was a band of colors. One end was a deep red, which merged into orange, then yellow, green, blue and violet. Then he placed another prism, with its faces opposite the first, and when the band of colors passed through it, it came out as white light again. What Newton proved was that white light consists of all the colors. He next tried to pass a single color through a prism, to see if it would divide into more parts. It did not. He found that each color is a pure light that cannot be broken. Thus white light is a mixture of pure colored light.

Long before Newton, in the book of Genesis, we have a description of light being broken into its spectrum of color, by tiny water droplets in the atmosphere—a rainbow.

The story, though often told to children, is not a mythical tale. The great flood catastrophe really did happen. The evidences it has left in the Earth are still there to verify the fact.

Noah had been in the Ark for 370 days. The Ark was the means of salvation for Noah and his family. All who were not in the Ark perished. The 370 days in the Ark pictures man's salvation in Jesus Christ, whose basic root number is 37 (See Appendix I). If we were to state those days in hours it would be 8,880 (370 x 24 = 8,880). The name *Jesus* has the number equivalent of 888. The 8,880 hours that Noah and his family were protected from death, by the Ark, was a transition to a new beginning, as is characterized by the number 8 (*beginning,* אך = 8).

The Apostle Peter recalled those renowned events, and inseparably linked them to Jesus when he described: *"An Ark, in which a few, that is, eight souls were saved by water."* In the original Greek text it reads, *κιβωτου εις ην ολιγοι τουτ εστιν οκτω ψυχαι διεσωθησαν δι υδατος,* and it adds to 8,880 – the same as the number of hours they were in the Ark.

At the end of those 8,880 hours, the 8 persons who were in the Ark emerged into a silent world—a new beginning.

LET THERE BE LIGHT

Every living creature, not having found refuge in the Ark, had been destroyed by the flood of waters. The sky was beginning to clear, and the sunlight shone upon the misty sky, forming the huge arc of a rainbow. It was a *sign* that a promise had been made–a promise by God that never again would he cause a flood to destroy the Earth. The *sign* was *light*–light from the Sun, which was broken into its spectrum of color by the tiny drops of rain in the air.

From the stance of the viewer (Noah and his family), the bow of color appeared to form a half circle, reaching from the sky to the ground, a full 180°. The Hebrew word *shine forth,* הופיעה, when multiplied by the 180°, produces 3,168. Their new beginning was to illustrate mankind's new beginning in the Lord Jesus Christ, whose number is 3,168.

The rainbow that reached across the sky was a beautiful sight to behold. It was a display of the colors of visible light– white light. The colors were arranged in the order of the spectrum, red at the top, followed by orange, yellow, green blue and violet.

Each of the colors of white light are determined by the length of the light wave. The units commonly used for this measurement are the *millimicron,* which is denoted by the symbol $\mu\mu$, which equals one millionth of a millimeter; and the Angstrom unit (A.U.), which is one ten millionth of a millimeter. In the table below I have converted these to inches.

	$\mu\mu$	A.U.	Inch
Red	710	7,100	.00000284
Orange	620	6,200	.00000248
Yellow	570	5,700	.00000228
Green	520	5,200	.00000208
Blue	470	4,700	.00000188
Violet	410	4,100	.00000164
		aggregate	.00001320

These numbers are derived from the center of each color range, giving the truest color.

When these colors are combined in the precisely proper amounts, all apparent color disappears, and the result is white. When all the lengths of the light waves are added, the aggregate is .00001320 of an inch. The number 132 is the addition of the letter-numbers for the word *white* in Hebrew (לבנים). It is a number that is basic to the number code of the Creator, as we shall see in the next chapter.

The visible white light from the Sun is the means of all life on Earth. It beautifully represents the Elohim, the Creator. And not surprisingly its spectrum of color bears the numbers of his name.

Red .00000284

284   *God, (Theos),* $\Theta \varepsilon o \varsigma$

2840   *The God of our fathers,* ο $\Theta \varepsilon o \varsigma$ $\tau \omega v$ $\pi \alpha \tau \varepsilon \rho \omega v$ (Acts 3:13)

2840   *I form the light, I create darkness; I make peace, and create evil; I the Lord do all these things,*
ובורא חשך עשה שלום ובורא רע אני יהוה עשה כל אלה
יוצר אור (Isaiah 45:7)

Orange .00000248

248   *The image of God,* בצלם אלהים (Genesis 1:27)

Yellow .00000228

228   *The Lord God Most High,* יהוה אלה עליון

228   *Firstborn* (referring to the only begotten Son of the Father), בכור (Psalm 89:27)

Green .00000208

208   *The Most High,* $v \psi \iota \sigma \tau o v$

Blue .00000188

188   *The beauty of Jehovah,* בנעם יהוה

1880   *The Most High,* υψιστος

Violet .00000164

164   *God the Great King,* אל מלך גדול

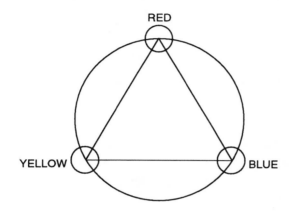

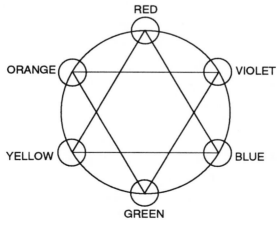

BEGINNINGS

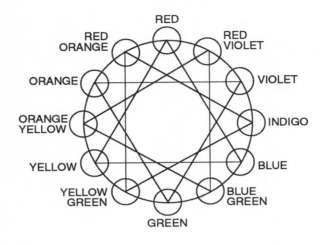

The range of visible light divides first into 3, then 6, then 12.

These 12-fold colors are merely the blending of the 3 primary colors. The spectrum, however, is generally stated as the 6 obvious colors of the rainbow: red, orange, yellow, green, blue and violet.

Man had been on the Earth 1,656 years before Noah entered the Ark and the flood of waters came. It marked the ending of an era and a new beginning. The rainbow of color, spreading the light from the Sun in a circle that engulfed the Earth, connected the Sun (God) and Earth (man) in a covenant. The solar number 864, when combined with the Earth number, 792, totals 1,656 – the number of years between man's beginning (Adam), and man's new beginning (the flood).

Noah was in the Ark 370 days, slightly over a year, putting him into the 1,658th year from Adam. When we use the *key,* 528, we see the beautiful relationship of the rainbow (a perfect circle), engulfing the Earth in its promise.

LET THERE BE LIGHT

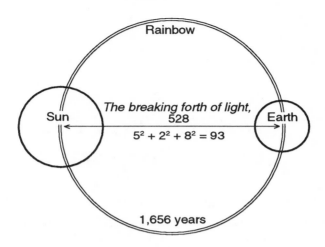

diameter   528
circumference   1,656

$5^2 + 2^2 + 8^2 = 93$
Light travels from Sun to Earth
93,000,000 miles

6
Creation and the Golden Proportion

The Golden Proportion, sometimes called the Divine Proportion, has come down to us from the beginning of creation. The harmony of this ancient proportion, built into the very structure of creation, can be unlocked with the *key,* מפתח, 528, opening to us its marvelous beauty.

Plato called it the most binding of all mathematical relations, and the key to the physics of the cosmos. It was the relationship of *El* to *Elohim.* The first act of creation, a *"breaking forth of light,"* כשחר, 528, was the division of Unity. A very special kind of division, in which 1 (Unity) can be expressed in two terms. In geometry, this occurs only when the smaller term is to the larger term as the larger term is to the smaller plus the larger. That may sound confusing, but it can be illustrated very simply.

Divide a line

A _____ B

at a point C

A _____ C _____ B

in such a way that the whole line AB is
longer than AC in the same proportion
as AC is longer than CB.

90

CREATION AND THE GOLDEN PROPORTION

To a mathematician, the Golden Proportion is written a:b::b:(a+b), thus the largest term (a+b) is a wholeness, or unit, composed of the sum of the other two terms. Thus when Unity is divided, that which is separated becomes part of the whole. The ratio is 1:1.618.

In mathematics, the Greek letter ϕ (pronounced phi) is used as a symbol of this proportion. It seems a fitting symbol, since Unity is expressed as a circle, and ϕ is a circle with a dividing line through it. It is the most intimate relationship that the created can have with the Creator—the primal or first division of One.

This unity of the *El* and *Elohim* was described by the Apostle John when telling of creation. Looking closely at the way he phrased it, we can see the geometric implications of the Golden Proportion—the division of One so that One retains its wholeness and unity with that which was divided. The Greek text reads, *"In the beginning was the Word, and the Word was with the God, and God was the Word,"* (John 1:1)

Some add the indefinite article before *"God"* in the last phrase, rendering it *"and a God was the Word."* However, no indefinite article exists in Greek. Whether we add the indefinite article or not, the meaning is the same. It describes the Golden Proportion.

The phrase *"the Word was with the God,"* has a deeper meaning in Greek. The word προς here translated *"with"* is a preposition that carries the thought of *"in"* or *"within."* Realizing this meaning of the word προς *(pros)*, it is apparent that John was alluding to the principle of the Golden Proportion. The division of One retained its oneness—the *Elohim* was both God and the Word.

The Apostle John, using this symbol, tied it to creation. *"All things were made by Him; and without Him was not anything made that was made. In Him was life; and the life was the light of men."*

The Greek word for *"all things,"* used in the text, is *panta,* παντα, and is also translated *"universe."* It bears the number 432 which relates to the Sun, it being the Sun's radius (432,000 miles).

To further show that John was calling the Word a God, he said (verse 18) *"No man hath seen God at any time; the only begotten Son (Θεος, God), which is in the bosom of the Father, he hath declared him."* (From the Nestle Greek Text.) The use of Θεος in the text clearly calls him a God, within the bosom of the Father. (It is interesting that the word *bosom* in Hebrew, צלחת, bears the number of the *key,* 528 – *(the breaking forth of light.*) But this God was a begotten God, begotten by the division of Unity, which retained its oneness, the Golden Proportion.

The *key,* 528, unlocks this beautiful proportion, showing *the breaking forth of light* (כשחר, 528) – the first act of creation.

A square whose perimeter is 5,280 will have sides of 1,320. We saw in the previous chapter that the number 1,320 is the aggregate of the wave lengths of the 6 basic colors of the spectrum of white light. 1320 is also the number of the Hebrew word for *white.* These two numbers are inseparably linked to light and the process of creation through photosynthesis. Remember, we found these basic numbers to be 15, 6 and 12 – the numbers involved in the process of photosynthesis. These numbers, 15, 6 and 12 are also basic to 5,280 and 1,320.

CREATION AND THE GOLDEN PROPORTION

$$5 + 2 + 8 = \mathbf{15}$$
$$1 + 3 + 2 = \mathbf{6}$$
$$5{,}280 + 1{,}320 = 2{,}136 \quad 2 + 1 + 3 + 6 = \mathbf{12}$$

$$5^2 + 2^2 + 8^2 = 93$$

Light travels from Sun to Earth 93 million miles.

Creation is growth by division. Genesis 1 shows 6 general divisions of creation, and divisions occurred within those 6, such as the dividing of light from darkness; and waters above from waters below; sea from land; and day from night. The number 132, when the digits are added, resolves to 6. Thus the statement, *"God divided,"* אלהים יבדל, logically adds to 132.

White light, 1,320, is to *the breaking forth of light,* 528, as one side of a square is to its perimeter. Thus a square with one side of 1,320 will have a perimeter of 5,280, linking the two concepts as a unit.

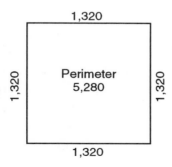

If this square were projected to show its Golden Proportion, we simply multiply 1,320 x $1/\phi = 816$. Then add the 816

to the 1,320, and one side of the rectangle will be the Golden Proportion. Now we have a Golden Rectangle, and a very special one. One that describes the Creator and His creation.

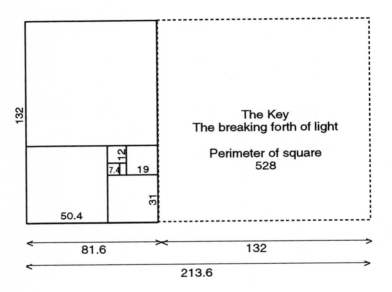

When a Golden Rectangle is divided into a square, that portion left over is another Golden Rectangle. Divide that one into a square and the portion left over will be another Golden Rectangle, continuing to infinity. The above rectangle has been divided into 7 Golden Rectangles. The geometry bears numbers that are absolutely startling in their description of the Creator and His creation, the Earth and man.

First rectangle, 132

132   *Jehovah your God,* יהוה אלהיכם, (Josh. 4:5)
132   *White,* לבנים (white light)

94

132   *A God of gods,* אלה אלהין (Dan. 2:47)

132   *To make whole,* ιαομαι

1320   *The fruit of thy womb* (Jesus), καρπος της κοιλιας

1320   *Man,* ανθρωποις

1320   *He made him (man) in the likeness of God,*
       בדמות אלהים עשה אתו (Gen. 5:1)

132   God divided, אלהים יבדל

<u>Second rectangle, 81.6</u>

(816 is an anagram of the speed of light, 186)

816   *His dominion,* ממשלתו (Psalm 103:22)

<u>Third rectangle, 50.4</u>

5,040 miles, combined radii of Earth and Moon

By addition:

504   *The fountain of living waters* (Jehovah),
       מקור מים חיים (Jer. 2:13)

540   *The True God,* αληθης Θεος (John 3:33)

540   *With my hands I stretched out the heavens,*
       אני ידי נטו שמים (Isa. 45:12)

By multiplication:

504   *Christ,* Χριστος

504   *World,* עולם

504   *His works* (God's creation), מעשיו

54   *The whole earth,* בל הארץ (Isa. 14:7)

54   *Jehovah your Redeemer,* יהוה גאלד (Isa. 48:17)

Fourth rectangle, 31

31   *God* (El), אל

310   *Brightness,* יקר

Fifth rectangle, 19

1,900 *Jehovah made the heavens and the earth,*

       (Ex. 20:11) עשה והיה את השמים ואת הארץ

190   *The God of old,* אלהי קדם (Deut. 33:27)

Sixth rectangle, 12

By addition:

120   *The King, Jehovah,* למלך (Zech. 14:17)

120   *Foundation,* מוסדי (Psalm 82:6)

120   *Perfection,* מכלל

By multiplication:

120   *The Key,* $\kappa\lambda\epsilon\iota\delta\alpha$ (Luke 11:52)

12   *Light* (referring to Jesus), אור (Isa. 9:2)

120   *The Living God,* אלהא חיא (Dan. 6:26)

120   *White,* לבנים

12   *Sun,* אור

12   *Almighty,* שדי

120   *All things (Universe),* $\pi\alpha\nu\tau\alpha$

Seventh rectangle, 7.4

74   *Foundation,* יסד

740   *You have laid the foundation of the Earth,* הארין יסדת

740   *Creation,* $\kappa\tau\iota\sigma\iota\varsigma$

74   *A great God,* אל גדול (Psalm 95:3)

These dimensions of the Golden Rectangle that are based on the *key, 528, the breaking forth of light,* are startling in their relationship to the Creator and his creation, including Earth and man.

Within the Golden Rectangle can be drawn a spiral, connecting the corners of the squares by the quadrants of a circle drawn within each square. This is known as the Golden Spiral. It appears throughout all creation. Some of the better known occurrences of this precise spiral in nature are the spiral of the seed pattern of the sunflower, the swirl of hair on the crown of the human head, the spiral of the nautilus shell, and the spiral of the galaxy of which our Solar System is a part.

Let's connect the corners of our Golden Rectangle and draw the spiral. On the basis of the dimensions of the rectangles, the length of the spiral will measure 3,168. Amazing! The number 3,168 is the number value for Lord Jesus Christ, and it also defines the perimeter of a square drawn around man's home, Earth (31,680 miles).

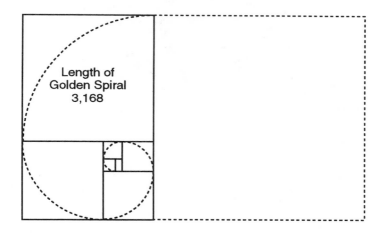

Length of
Golden Spiral
3,168

The numbers that define the rectangles and the spiral are magnificent–and they are based upon the square that holds the *key, the breaking forth of light,* 528. The probability of such a relationship occurring by chance is not worthy of computing, nor is the probability that I simply devised it for purposes of writing an interesting book, (I'm not that intelligent, nor am I a mathematician). We are dealing with evidence of a Divine Creator, a Designer who has woven His designs into all of his Creation.

The arrangement of the seed pattern of the sunflower are interwoven Golden Spirals (left and right).

CREATION AND THE GOLDEN PROPORTION

The world around us is replete with Golden Spirals. We pass by them every day, we walk over them, we see them in the sky at night, and they are an integral part of the shape of the human body. They all bear the signature of the Lord Jesus Christ.

Recently, while walking through a dense pine forest with some friends, I stooped to pick up a cone that lay in the trail. The bottom portion of the cone had not opened normally, and still enclosed its seeds. The spiral of its design was flawless. I mused on the joy of holding in my hand the same Divine Proportion that is intrinsic to the spinning galaxy that houses our Solar System—a design that bears the signature of its Creator.

The seven rectangles, shown to produce the Golden Spiral with its identifying number, 3,168, also bear the number of their Maker by their perimeters.

Perimeters of rectangles:

1	427.2
2	264.0
3	163.2
4	100.8
5	62.3
6	38.5
7	23.8
Total	1,079.8, or 1,080

The first 6 rectangles through which the Golden Spiral passes have aggregate perimeters of 1,056, while all 7 add to 1,080. Both numbers are beautiful in their relation to the Creator and the creation. The number 1,056 shows its link with the first acts of creation in Isaiah 45:7: *"I form the light, I create darkness."* The Hebrew text is יוצר אור ובורא חשך, and adds to 1,056.

The man Jesus Christ, the first and only-begotten part of the Elohim, came to Earth to bring the gift of salvation to man. This is why the Apostle Paul referred to Him as *"the heavenly man,"* (I Cor. 15:48). He used the Greek words *o επουρανιος,* which adds to 1,056. (1,056 x 3 = 3,168, *Lord Jesus Christ.)* This act of sending a Saviour to Earth to redeem man was prophesied by Isaiah (19:20): *"He shall send them a Saviour, and a great One."* The text in Hebrew reads ישלח להם מושיע ורב, and adds to 1,056. The Psalmist, David, mentioned the same wonderful gift to man: *"The joy of thy salvation,"* ששון ישעך, which also adds to 1,056. Daniel, referring to the fact of Elohim's royal authority and power, said, *"His dominion is an everlasting dominion that shall not pass away,"* (Dan. 7:14) It adds to 1,056.

The total of all 7 rectangles is the magnificent number 1,080. Since zeros are merely place holders, in gematria they can be added or deleted without changing the significance of the number. The number is simply a 1 and an 8. The 1 represents Unity, the beginning of creation, while 8 represents a new beginning through Jesus Christ. 8, as it is used in the gematria of both the Hebrew and Greek text has reference to Jesus (*Jesus* adds to 888), and the work of salvation which provides a new beginning for man.

Below are some of the ways 18 (1 and 8) are used in the scriptures.

By addition:

180   *Maker,* (referring to the Creator), פעל

18   *He who lives* (Jehovah), חי (Dan. 12:7)

1800 *I am the living One,* εγω ειμι ο ζων (Rev. 1:17)

18 *Life,* חי

108 *Red* (the color in the spectrum that bears the number for *Theos,* God) חכלילי

1008 *The work of thy fingers* (creation), מעשה אצבעתיך (Psalm 8:3)

1080 *The Holy Spirit,* πνευμα το αγιον

1080 *Heaven is my throne and the Earth is my footstool,* (showing God's ownership and rulership in both heaven and Earth) (Isaiah 66:1)

1080 *God himself that formed the Earth and made it,* הוא האלהים יצר הארץ ועשה, (Isaiah 45:18)

1080 *The Lord is in His holy temple, let all the Earth keep silence before him,* יהוה בהיכל קדשו הם מפניו כל הארץ, (Hab. 2:20)

1008 *The Lord is high above all nations, and His glory above the heavens,* רם על כל גוים יהוה על השמים כבודו (Psa. 113:4)

108 *Two parts* (the two parts of Elohim as shown in the Golden Proportion, the dividing of Unity), חצי

By multiplication (zeros dropped):

18 *Majesty,* גדלה

108 *Majesty,* גדולה

18 *Your Redeemer,* גאלך

108 *Truth,* αληθεια

18 *Holy Father,* πατερ αγιε

18 *Great,* μεγαλα

18 *Perfection,* כליל

1008 *Tree of life* (in Eden), עץ החיים (Gen. 2:9)

108 *Judge* (of all the earth), השפט (Gen. 18:25)

18	*The throne of Jehovah,* כסא יהוה (Jer. 3:17)
18	*Jehovah your God,* יהוה אלהיכם (Josh. 4:5)
108	*Salvation,* פליטה (Joel 2:32)
108	*The King, Jehovah,* למלך יהוה (Zech. 14:17)
1008	*Kingdom of God,* βασιλειαν αυτου
1008	*Christ,* Χριστου
1008	*His work* (creation), פעלו (Deut. 32:4)
108	God, צור
108	*Maker,* יצרו (Isa. 45:9)
108	*The majesty of Jehovah,* גאות יהוה (Isa. 26:10)
108	*To make reconciliation,* ιλασκεσθαι (Heb. 2:17)
108	*The brightness of His light,* ונגה כאור תהיה (Hab. 3:4)
1008	*Holiness,* αγιοτης
1008	*The Holy One of Jacob,* קדוש יעקב (Isa. 29:23)
18	God, Θεων
1008	*The Gift of God* (Jesus), δωρεαν Θεου (John 4:10)

The list is impressive! The importance of the numbers 1 and 8 is clear. It is fitting, then, that the hydrogen atom, which represents *El,* has the atomic weight of 1.0080. And it does not go unnoticed that the radius of the Moon is 1,080 miles, while the combined diameters of Earth and Moon measure 10,080 miles.

The relationship of 1 and 8 to light and perfection is easily seen.

$1 + 8 = 9$ (the number of wholeness and perfection)

$1,008 - 108 = 900 \times 2 = 1,800$

$1,008 + 108 = 1116$ (light travels 11,160,000 miles per minute)

$1,008 \div 108 = 9.3$ (9.333)

CREATION AND THE GOLDEN PROPORTION

(Light comes 93 million miles to Earth)

$9.333 \div 108 = .0864$ (Solar number)

$1,008 \times 108 = 108,864$

— Solar number

——— *Elohim* (Maker, Creator)

The above exercise in numbers makes apparent the inter-relationship of the Elohim, light, and the Sun. It is an integral part of the design built into all creation as shown in the Golden Proportion. The numbers of the proportion (.618), as well as being an anagram of the speed of light (186), bear the numbers of the Creator.

618   *I am the First,* אני ראשן (Isa. 48:12)

618   *El, the God of Israel,* אל אלהי ישראל (Gen. 33:20)

618   *He is the God of gods and the Lord of lords, God the great, the mighty,* האלהים ואדני האדנים האל הגדל הגבר הוא אלהי (Deut. 10:17)

618   *Jehovah shall be King over all the earth,* על כל הארץ והיה יהוה למלך (Zech. 14:9)

2x618   *God with us* (the meaning of the name Emmanuel) μεθ ημων Θεος (Matt. 1:23)

2x618   *A Root out of dry ground* (Jesus), שרש מארץ ציה (Isa. 53:2)

4x618   *The scepter shall not depart from Judah, nor a lawgiver from between his feet, until Shiloh come, and to Him shall the gathering of the people be.*

שבט מיהודה ומחקק מבין רגליו עד כי יבא שילה ולו יקהת עמים לא יסור (Gen. 49:10)

The beautiful relationship of the Golden Proportion to

creation can be shown by the inverse of the numbers. Reading it from right to left, as in Hebrew, it would be 816. We have already seen that 816 is the number value of *"His dominion"* (all of God's realm) − 816 ÷ 618 = 1,320, the basic number involved in creation, the number of white light, and the process of growth by division (*"God divided,"* 132).

The Golden Spiral defines a mathematical progression known as the Fibonacci numbers, named after their discoverer, Leonardo Fibonacci, in the 12th century A.D. The progression is simple, yet profound, because it is found throughout all creation. It begins with 1 (the number of Unity). And, as we observed with the hydrogen atom, the 1 divides and becomes two Ones in the hydrogen molecule, representing the Elohim. In the Fibonacci series, the two Ones are added, making 2. Then the last two numbers are always added together, producing the next number. Thus the numbers become:

1 1 2 3 5 8 13 21 34 55 89 144 etc.

This beautiful proportional progression is found throughout nature. We witness it every day, but are not aware of it.

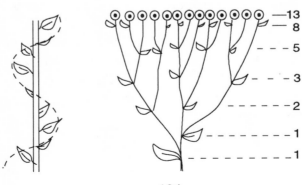

104

CREATION AND THE GOLDEN PROPORTION

The arrangement of leaves on the stems of plants often follows the Fibonacci progression.

The progression of this spiral can be seen in the mollusk shell–the size increases as the mollusk grows, but the shape is unaltered. And this is the basic principle of the spiral–it can grow but its basic shape remains the same.

Because the Golden Proportion is built into man, and his relation to Earth (man's home), it helps us to understand the fact that man was made in the *"image and likeness"* of his Creator.

The drawing by Leonardo da Vinci shows the human figure, divided in half at the sex organ and by ϕ at the navel. Thus the sex organ, the means of human reproduction, is at the center of the square, while the navel, that which connected him to his life-giver, is at the center of the circle. It is the same proportion of circle and square that defines the relationship of Earth and Moon.

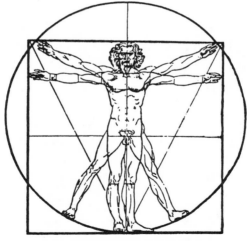

Center of circle at navel.
Center of square at sex organ.

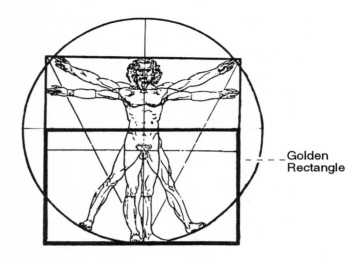

When a human child is born, his navel defines the halfway point of his body, but when he reaches adulthood, the navel defines ϕ, and the sex organ is at the halfway point, or the center of the square.

This relationship of man to his home, Earth, and to his Creator is not a chance encounter. It was the beautiful design of a Master Designer.

The first division of creation recorded in Genesis 1 (pertaining to Earth), was dividing light and darkness. *"God divided between light and darkness, and God called the light day, and the darkness he called night."* The gematria for *day* and *night* reveal the Golden Proportion.

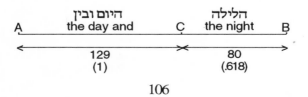

CREATION AND THE GOLDEN PROPORTION

The second division was of water. He divided the waters above the expanse from the waters below the expanse. The wording of the text defines the Golden Proportion.

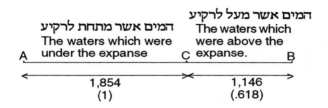

The total gematria of the text is 3,000. Thus if this proportion were used for the Golden Rectangle, its perimeter would be 6,000, and the spiral drawn within it would measure 1,800 – the numbers of beginning.

Realizing the amazing relationship of the Golden Rectangle to its Golden Spiral, I checked them for other meaningful numbers in the gematria of the Hebrew and Greek scriptures. What I found was astounding! If the long side of a Golden Rectangle (its Golden Proportion) is a sacred number, the length of its spiral will also be a sacred number. A few choice examples are listed below. The formula is simple. Multiply the length of the rectangle by 2.4, the product is the length of the spiral of its 6 divisions.

Golden Rectangle	Golden Spiral
370	888
60	144
180	432
360	864
1,480	3,552
420	1,008
310	744
27	576
12	288

The occurrences of these numbers in the gematria of the scriptures are many. For the purposes of this example, I will be as brief as possible, while still showing the importance and obvious intent of the Designer.

370   is a prime that is basic to most of the titles of Elohim, as listed in Appendix I

888   *Jesus, Ιησους*

60   As has been shown, 6 is basic to creation, light, and photosynthesis.

144   A number basic to creation and the New Creation, believers (see Appendix II)

180   The 1 and 8 are the numbers of beginning.

432   *All things (Universe), παντα (panta)*

360   The basic definition of a circle. *God,* אלה

864   The solar number. Also the number for *God, Θεων*

1480   *Christ, Χριστος*

3552   *Author of eternal salvation,*
αιτιος σωτηριας αιωνιου

420   (42) *God,* אלוה

1008   *The work of thy fingers* (creation), מעשה אצבעתיך
(Also the atomic weight of hydrogen, 1.0080)

310   (31) *God,* אל *(El)*

744   *Two great lights* (Sun and Moon), המאורת הגדלים

27   *Light* (207), אור

576   *Spirit, πνευμα*

576   *He who made the Plieades and Orion,* עשה כימה וכסיל
(Amos 5:8)

12   (120) *Foundation,* מוסדי

288   (2880) *The Kingdom of Heaven,*

CREATION AND THE GOLDEN PROPORTION

These are but a brief example of the use of the Golden Proportion in the gematria of the scriptures, there are many, many more. It appears to be intrinsic to the sacred design.

The Golden Proportion has been studied for centuries, and found to be the basis of all physical beauty. We seem to respond instinctively to it, as if it were a bond between man and his environment–a binding covenant of love between the Creator and His creation.

When the only-begotten Son of God came to Earth, to become a baby, born in the little town of Bethlehem, it was a binding of heaven and Earth by the Golden Proportion. Bethlehem is positioned on our globe at the latitude of 31.68°N, a position that forms a Golden Rectangle with the polar and equatorial diameters of the Earth.

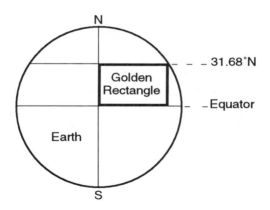

The Golden Proportion is the basis of the design of the 5-pointed star–the pentagram. Each of its points are connected by lines that are precisely divided into segments, one measuring 1 and the other measuring .618, making the whole line 1.618.

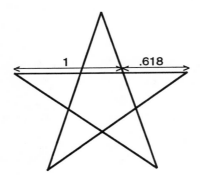

Because of the relationship of the pentagram to the Golden Proportion *(φ)*, the Pythagoreans wore it as a symbol of their society. Pythagoras, however, did not invent, nor discover it. The pentagram was used by the Babylonians and the Egyptians long before Pythagoras. But its beautiful display of the Golden Proportion tells us that it is part of the fabric of creation.

A 5-pointed star is not easy to draw. One method is to begin with a square whose sides are 1 (Unity).

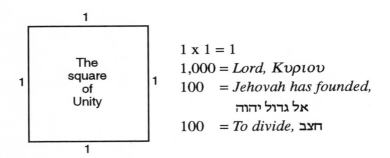

$1 \times 1 = 1$

$1,000 = $ *Lord, Κυριου*

$100 \quad = $ *Jehovah has founded,*

אל גדול יהוה

$100 \quad = $ *To divide,* חצב

Next, we extend one side of the square to form a Golden Rectangle.

CREATION AND THE GOLDEN PROPORTION

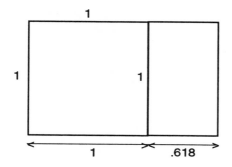

Using the Golden Rectangle as the base, with compass and straightedge a pentagon can be drawn that will have sides of 1.

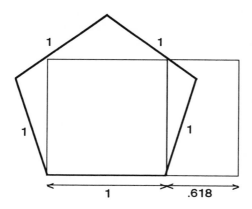

Let's assign a unit to the 1. Because we have seen how the mile unit is the *key,* 528, let's apply that key to unlock the message within the pentagon. If one side now equals 1 mile (5,280 feet), the perimeter of the pentagon will be 316,800 inches. It bears the number of *Lord Jesus Christ, Κυριος Ιησους Χριστος,* 3,168. The perimeter stated in yards will be 79,200, which is the Earth number (7,920).

111

The perimeter of the original square will be 21,120 feet. The gematria of this number tells of the sending of the only-begotten Son to Earth to be man's Redeemer.

> 2,112 *A virgin shall conceive and bear*
> *a son and shall call his name*
> *Emmanuel.* (Isaiah 7:14)

The height of the pentagon will be 1.53884 miles. Draw a square on the height (1.53884^2) and it will contain 2.368 square miles.

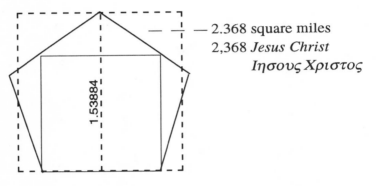

— $\frac{\quad}{\quad}$ — 2.368 square miles
2,368 *Jesus Christ*
     Ιησους Χριστος

A circle superscribed on the pentagon will have a circumference of 5.40 miles.

100	*To divide,* חצב	
540	*Holy God,* אלהים קדשים	(Josh. 24:19)
504	*To divide* (in half), חצות	
540	*The whole Earth* (by multiplication),	
	כל הארץ	(Isa. 14:7)
172	*Jehovah our King,* יהוה מלכנו	(Isa. 33:22)
172	*To divide,* בקע	

CREATION AND THE GOLDEN PROPORTION

86   *Elohim,* אלהים

86   *Dividing,* מבדיל (Genesis 1:6)

1080   *God himself that formed the Earth and made it*
        הוא האלהים יצר הארץ ועשה (Isaiah 45:18)

108   *Divide* (two parts), חצי

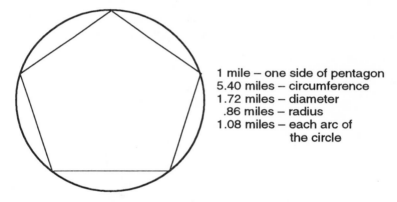

1 mile – one side of pentagon
5.40 miles – circumference
1.72 miles – diameter
.86 miles – radius
1.08 miles – each arc of
          the circle

Within the circle we can now draw a 5-pointed star, connecting the points. Each connecting line is a Golden Proportion.

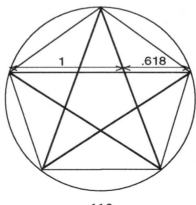

Notice that the gematria for these "divisions" of Unity keeps referring to the act of dividing. The primal act of creation was the dividing of Unity.

If we used the circle that is superscribed on the pentagon whose side is 1, and projected it into an exact image of itself, as has been shown by the hydrogen molecule–the dividing of Unity–the vesica that is formed will have a width of .86. The two overlapping circles, as we saw in chapter 1, represent the Elohim (Father and Son). The letter-numbers in the name *Elohim,* אלהים, add to 86.

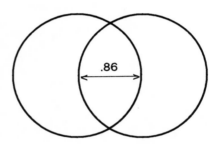

86 = *Elohim,* אלהים

The primal act of growth by division, the basic principle of creation, is displayed in each of the circles.

1	One side of pentagon
100	*To divide,* חצב
5.40	Circumference of circle
504	*To divide* (in half), חצות
1.72	Diameter of circle
172	*To divide,* בקע

.86   Radius of circle

86   *Dividing,* מבדיל

1.08   Each arc of circle

108   *Divide* (two parts), חצי

There is no way that such harmony could be by blind random chance. It displays the hand of an amazing Designer.

What an awesome Creator! He planted in man, not only the mathematical proportions that harmonize with the Universe, but he included the ability to perceive and appreciate that beauty. Surely the appreciation of beauty must be an integral part of the Creator, for we were made in his likeness. He, himself, must be the very personification of mathematical beauty and harmony.

7
The Sound of Music

Just as the Golden Proportion pertains to sight, so it also pertains to sound.

We have seen the fact that the number 132 relates to man and his Creator–man having been made in the likeness of his Creator. Man was created perfect, or whole–a reflection of his Maker. The gematria tells the story.

132   *Jehovah your God,* יהוה אלהיכם
1320   *Man, ανθρωποις* (anthropos) (the first Adam)
132   *Make whole, ιαομαι*
132   *White,* לבנים (white light)
1320   *The fruit of thy womb* (Jesus) (the second Adam)
       καρπος της κοιλιας
132   *God divided,* אלהים יבדל (Genesis 1)

The number 132, which is basic to creation, to light, and to man, is also basic to music.

C above Middle C
528 vibrations per second

Middle C
264 vibrations per second

C below Middle C
132 vibrations per second

THE SOUND OF MUSIC

The sounds that are harmonious to the human ear are based in the numbers 7 and 11. However, we think in terms of 8, the octave, which in reality is 7 plus a new beginning, bringing us to 8. The 8, of course, is really the beginning, or 1 of the next series of 7. The octave was not an invention of man. It occurs naturally as the first and second partials of sounds usually considered to be musical.

The laws of musical harmony were not invented by man, they were discovered. Those laws reflect the underlying harmony in all creation, just as the harmony of number was not man's invention, but rather an intrinsic part of creation. Those who recognize such harmonies are enriched with a sense of the beauty of the Creator.

The experience of beauty, either of sight or of sound, touches an awareness deep within us that there is a unity and harmony in nature, of which we are a part. Our response to beauty is an intrinsic part of our being. It is an inherent response to our Creator.

The words pertaining to sound, in Hebrew, bear numbers that relate to the Creator.

המלה, *Sound* = 80
המולה, *Sound* = 86

80   *To make perfect,* כלל
86   *Elohim,* אלהים

The vibration that is created when a string is plucked begins as a unit, then it divides into two parts, three parts, four parts, and on toward infinity. Each part gives a separate tone, each in harmony. To our awareness it sounds as one harmonious resonate tone. What we are hearing is really the initial tone plus its overtones.

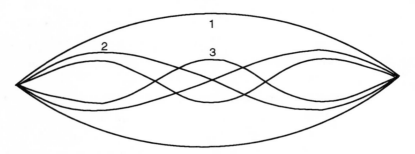

When a string is plucked 1 indicates the
initial tone – 2 and 3 indicate the overtones
that produce harmonics.

The number 1 represents Unity. Pythagoras maintained that 1 is not a number at all, but the expression of Unity which, by dividing, gives birth to all other numbers. This is true of sound. The full length of the string is 1, Unity, and when plucked, gives birth to the successive numbers to infinity by its overtones.

If the rate of vibration ranges between approximately $10H_z$ (vibrations per second) and 20,000 H_z, it can be referred to as acoustic vibration, for if these vibrations are transmitted to the human ear, they will produce the sensation of sound. There are vibrations that are too low, as well as too high, for the human ear to receive as sound.

When a string is plucked, the first overtone is a note an octave higher. It is inherent within the first and second tone. Man did not invent it, he only named it. He called it an octave–the eighth tone on the diatonic scale. The octave occurs naturally in the voices of men and women. Generally when men and women sing a melody together, the natural difference between their respective voices is an octave. These

118

two tones are so completely interwoven that they are given the same letter name. Thus from C to C is an octave–8 notes. It is 7 tones, leading naturally to the 8th, which is really the first of the next series.

By international agreement, in 1955, the frequency of the note A was determined to be 440 H$_z$. This standardizes all the instruments of the world. Thus a musician can travel to any area of the world and his instruments will be in tune with the local instruments.

Basically there are four different tuning systems, all built around the use of A as 440 H$_z$. They differ only slightly in extreme upper and lower ranges, for purposes of orchestral agreement. However, the natural tuning is called "Just." The Just tuning is in perfect harmony with the sacred numbers of the gematria of the Hebrew and Greek scriptures, and the geometry of Creation.

On the next page is a chart of the musical scale (diatonic), beginning with C below Middle C, and going up to the 5th octave above Middle C, (7 octaves, or 7 sevens), with the intervals between tones. Note that each tone is divisible by 11, and the intervals between tones are divisible by 11.

Counting from C, the perfect fifth would be G. All of the numbers in the G column are multiples of 12 and 18, and all resolve to 18.

198	11 x 18	1 + 9+ 8 = 18
396	22 x 18	3 + 9 + 6 = 18
792	44 x 18	7 + 9 + 2 = 18
1,584	88 x 18	1 + 5 + 8 + 4 = 18
3,168	176 x 18	3 + 1 + 6 + 8 = 18
6,336	352 x 18	6 + 3 + 3 + 6 = 18
12,672	704 x 18	1 + 2 + 6 + 7 + 2 = 18

All the numbers in the C column are multiples of 12 and 8.

C	Interval	D	Interval	E	Interval	F	Interval	G	Interval	A	Interval	B	Interval
1 below 132	16.5	148.5	16.5	165	11	176	22	198	22	220	27.5	247.5	16.5
Middle C 264	33	297	33	330	22	352	44	396	44	440	55	495	33
1 above 528	66	594	66	660	44	704	88	792	88	880	110	990	66
2 above 1056	132	1188	132	1320	88	1408	176	1584	176	1760	220	1980	132
3 above 2112	264	2376	264	2640	176	2816	352	3168	352	3520	440	3960	264
4 above 4224	528	4752	528	5280	352	5632	704	6336	704	7040	880	7920	528
5 above 8448	1056	9504	1056	10560	704	11264	1408	12672	1408	14080	1760	15840	1056

The inter-relationship of the numbers of music and the gematria of the Hebrew and Greek scriptures is awesome. Both were designed by the same Designer. In the interests of brevity, I list only a small portion of them below. Remember, in gematria, zeros can be deleted. It is the basic number that is intended.

All of these multiples of 11, shown in the chart, bear the following beautiful gematria.

11 x 1 = 11

11   *Earth,* γη

110   *Foundation,* מוסד

110   *Most High,* עלי

101   *Great is the glory of Jehovah,* גדול כבוד יהוה (Psa. 138:5)

1001   *Two lights* (Sun and Moon), שני מארת (Gen. 1:16)

11 x 2 = 22

220 *A sure foundation* (Jesus), מוסד מוסד (Isa. 28:16)
220 *Branch* (Jesus), סעיף

11 x 3 = 33

330 *Holy and Just One* (Jesus), αγιον και δικαιον
(Acts 3:14)
330 *He is the God of gods and Lord of lords,*
הוא אלהי האלהים ואדני האדנים (Deut. 10:17)
3030 *The Son of Man* (Jesus), ο υιος του ανθρωπου
(John 6:31)

11 x 4 = 44

44 *One God,* אל אחד (Mal. 2:10)
404 *One Lord and His name One,* יהוה אחד ושמו אחד
(Zech. 14:9)
440 *The Holy One,* לקדוש (Psalm 89:18)

11 x 5 = 55

55 *Foundation,* ארן
55 *Lord,* ארן

11 x 6 = 66

66 *The Lord,* האדון (Isa. 1:24)
66 *Your God,* אלהיך (Isa. 60:19)
660 *Advocate* (Jesus), παρακλητον (I John 2:1)

11 x 8 = 88

88 *A child is born* (Jesus), ילד ילד (Isa. 9:6)
88 *The majesty of Jehovah,* בגאון יהוה (Isa. 24:14)
808 *I am* (Jehovah), εγω

11 x 9 = 99

99   *Amen, αμην*

99   *The garden of the Lord* (Eden), כגן יהוה (Gen. 13:10)

909   *In beginning* (of creation), *αρχης* (II Pet. 3:4)

11 x 12 = 132

132   *Make whole, ιαομαι*

132   *Jehovah your God,* יהוה אלהיכם (Josh. 4:5)

132   *A God of gods,* אלה אלהין (Dan. 2:47)

1302   *The Creator, τον κτισαντα* (Rom. 1:25)

1320   *Made him* (man) *in the likeness of God,*
        בדמות אלהים עשה אתו (Gen. 5:1)

132   *God divided,* אלהים יברל (Genesis 1)

11 x 15 = 165

165   *The wonderful works of God, τα μεγαλεια του Θεου*
       (Acts 2:11)

165   *Just One* (Jesus), *δικαιον* (Acts. 22:14)

165   *Counsellor* (Jesus), עצה (Isa. 9:6)

11 x 16 = 176

176   *Garden of Eden,* ן בעדן (Gen. 2:8)

176   *God reigns,* מלך אלהים (Psalm 47:8)

176   *Shine forth* (God), הופיעה (Psa. 80:1)

11 x 24 = 264

264   *Truth, αληθειας*

264   *Signs, σημεια*

264   *The Light* (Jesus), *του φωτος* (John 1:7)

11 x 27 = 297

297   *A Branch of Righteousness* (Jesus) צמח נדקה

11 x 32 = 352

352   *The Way* (Jesus), η $o\delta o\varsigma$ (John 14:6)

352   *Light,* $\lambda \alpha \mu \pi \alpha \varsigma$

352   *The God great and awesome,* האל הגדול והנורא (Dan. 9:4)

352   *His name* (Jehovah), ושמו (Zech. 14:9)

11 x 45 = 495

495   *Son* (Mary called Jesus $\tau \varepsilon \kappa \nu o \nu$ - Luke 2:48)

11 x 48 = 528

528   *The Key,* מפתח

528   *The breaking forth of light,* כשחר

5028   *The Lamb slain from the foundation of the world,* $\tau o \nu$ $\alpha \rho \nu \iota o \nu$ $\tau o \nu$ $\varepsilon \sigma \varphi \alpha \gamma \mu \varepsilon \nu o \nu$ $\alpha \pi o$ $\kappa \alpha \tau \alpha \beta o \lambda \eta \varsigma$ $\kappa o \sigma \mu o \nu$ (Rev. 13:8)

11 x 54 = 594

594   *The Rock of Israel* (referring to the Bethel Stone, but prophetically to Jesus), אבן ישראל (Gen. 49:24)

11 x 64 = 704

704   *Pierced* (referring to Jesus), $\varepsilon \xi \varepsilon \kappa \varepsilon \nu \tau \eta \sigma \alpha \nu$ (Rev. 1:7)

704   *House of God,* $o \iota \kappa o \nu$ $\Theta \varepsilon o \nu$ (Matt. 12:4)

740   *The blood of Jesus,* $\alpha \iota \mu \alpha$ $I \eta \sigma o \nu$ (I John 1:7)

11 x 72 = 792

7,920 miles – diameter of Earth

792   *Jehovah, the Maker of the heavens,* יהוה עשה שמים (Psalm 121:2)

792   *He is salvation* (Jehovah), ישועות (Gen. 3:20)

11 x 96 = 1,056

1,056   *I form the light, I create darkness* (Jehovah),
יוצר אור ובורא חשך (Isa. 45:7)

1,056   *His dominion is an everlasting dominion that shall not pass away,* שלטנה שלטן עלם די לא יעדה (Dan. 7:14)

1,056   *The joy of thy salvation,* ששון ישעך (Psalm 51:12)

1,056 inches – The Reed given to Ezekiel in vision.

11 x 108 = 1,188

1,188   *Glory of God,* $\delta o \xi \alpha \ \tau o v \ \Theta \varepsilon o \varsigma$

1,188   *A minister* (Jesus), $\lambda \varepsilon \iota \tau o v \rho \gamma o \varsigma$ (Heb. 8:2)

11 x 128 = 1,408

1,408   *Saviour,* $\sigma \omega \tau \eta \rho$

1,408   *Voice* (of Jesus), $\phi \omega \nu \eta \nu$ (Rev. 1:10)

11 x 144 = 1,584

1,584   *In Isaac shall thy Seed by called* (prophetic of Jesus),
$\varepsilon \nu \ I \sigma \alpha \alpha \kappa \ \kappa \lambda \eta \theta \eta \sigma \varepsilon \tau \alpha \iota \ \sigma o \iota \ \sigma \pi \varepsilon \rho \mu \alpha$ (Rom. 9:7)

1,584   *I will establish my covenant,* והקמתי את בריתי (Gen. 9:11)

11 x 180 = 1,980

198   *He is altogether lovely* (prophetic of Jesus),
כלו מחמדים (Sol. 5:16)

198   *The King in his beauty* (Jesus), מלך ביפיו (Isa. 33:17)

19.8 inches – The Temple Cubit (used in the construction of Solomon's Temple)

11 x 192 = 2,112

2,112   *A virgin shall conceive and bear a son and shall call*
      His name Emmanuel,

העלמה הרה וילדת בן וקראת שמו עמנו אל (Isa. 7:14)

2,112   *Glory of the Lord,* δοξης του κυριου (II Thes. 2:14)

21.12 inches – The Great Cubit given to Ezekiel in vision.

11 x 288 = 3,168

3,168   *Lord Jesus Christ,* Κυριος Ιησους Χριστος

3,168   *Mediator between God and man* (Jesus),
      μεσιτης Θεου και ανθρωπων (I Tim. 2:5)

The list has been abridged in the interests of not burdening the reader. I have tried to choose the obviously significant ones. Each of the above numbers is the number of vibrations per second in the notes of the diatonic scale, or the interval between notes. They are all multiples of 11. Why 11?

Possibly it is the number that connects the whole function of music with the Creator, the Elohim. The two atoms of the hydrogen molecule, with their overlapping electron wave bubbles, each have 1 proton in their nucleus, representing the first act of creation—the *El* becoming the *Elohim*. It is fitting that the beautiful harmony of the Father and Son be conveyed through the harmony of music.

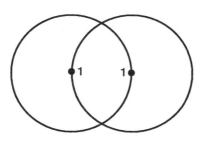

125

BEGINNINGS

*Jehovah possessed me in the beginning of His way,
before His works of old. I was set up from everlasting,
from the beginning, before the earth was.... When He
appointed the foundations of the earth, then I was by
Him, as one brought up with Him; and I was daily His
delight, rejoicing always before Him.*

(Proverbs 8:22-30)

That music should be evidence of the "harmony of beginning," is a precious gift to man!

Through the experiments of Hans Jenny, it was discovered that sound frequencies could cause random particles to assume geometric patterns. In *Sacred Geometry*, Robert Lawlor shows photographs of the action of sound frequencies.[1] An amazing pattern emerges. A circle will be transformed into a seven-fold figure, sometimes resembling a 7-pointed star, and sometimes a heptagon, and will always return to a circle. My attempt to illustrate these patterns is shown below.

---

1 Robert Lawlor, *Sacred Geometry,* The Crossroads Publishing Co., New York, 1982, p. 87.

THE SOUND OF MUSIC

As stated previously, music is dominated by the number 7. We think of it as 8, and call it the octave. The eighth note, however, is actually the first note in the next series of 7. Thus 8 and 1 become inseparable as the numbers of beginning.

The relationship of music to the heptagon is amazing, and within it we find the number 1.8 repeated. Draw a heptagon with sides of 1, and the lines by which each of the seven points are connected will be 1.8 each.

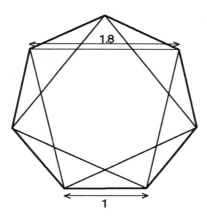

In music 1 and 8 both represent the beginning of each diatonic octave. These numbers of beginning, when raised to their triplet, describe the Beginner.

888   *Jesus, Ιησους*
888   *The Founder, ο οικιστης*
888   *I am the Life, ειμι η ζωη*
888   *The Light dwells in Him,* ונהירא עמה שרא (Dan. 2:22)

111   *Only Son* (Jesus), $\upsilon\iota o\varsigma\ \mu o\nu o\varsigma$ (John 3:16)

111   *Lord of all,* אדון כל (Zech. 6:5)

111   *The blood of Jesus,* $\tau o\ \alpha\iota\mu\alpha\ I\eta\sigma o\upsilon$ (I John 1:7)

111   *Wonderful* (prophetic name of Jesus), אלפ (Isa. 9:6)

Surely He has placed His signature on all His works. We have observed it in the Earth, Sun, and Moon; in the hydrogen molecule; in photosynthesis; in light, color and sound. These witnesses all tell the same story. They tell of a Beginner, a Designer, a Master Mathematician!

8
Three Witnesses

In the mouth of two or three witnesses shall every word be established. (II Corinthians 13:1)

The signature of the Designer has not only been displayed in all His creation, it can also be found in structures built by the hands of man. Although the construction was man's, the design reveals the hand of the Master Designer. Three of these structures are well known; but it is not well known that they hold the signature of the Architect.

The prophet Jeremiah told us where they are—well, sort of. He said:

The Great, the Mighty God, the Lord of Hosts is his name...who has set signs and wonders in the land of Egypt, even unto this day, and in Israel, and among other men. (Jer. 32:19, 20)

What is there in Egypt, Israel, and somewhere else in this world that bears witness of the Creator—witnesses that were in existence in Jeremiah's day?

The prophet Isaiah identified one of them.

In that day shall there be an altar to the Lord in the midst of the land of Egypt, and a pillar at the border thereof to the Lord. And it shall be for a sign and for a witness unto the Lord of hosts in the land of Egypt.
(Isa. 19:19,20)

129

There is only one spot on Earth that answers to that description. It is at the base of the quadrant of the Nile Delta. If a compass were used to trace the curve of the extremities of the Nile Delta, the compass point would be resting precisely on the Great Pyramid.

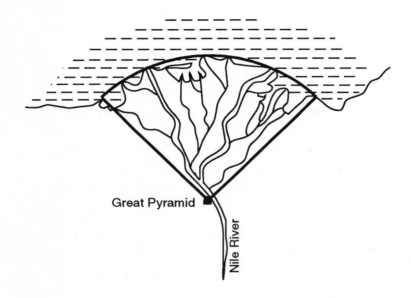

Great Pyramid

Nile River

The geographical identification of the "witness" tells us it is the Great Pyramid. But hidden in the description that Isaiah gave, is the precise height of the Pyramid. Add all of the letter-numbers of the text, and the total is 5,449. In recent years, men have been able to measure, with accuracy, the Great Pyramid. Its height, from its socket level base to its summit platform, is 5,448.960 Pyramid inches (a unit so close to the British Inch they are nearly identical). For all practical purposes, the number is 5,449.

130

Gematria for Isaiah 19:19-20

ביום	....	58
ההוא	....	17
יהיה	....	30
מזבח	....	57
ליהוה	....	56
בתוך	....	428
ארץ	....	291
מצרים	....	380
ומצבה	....	143
אצל	....	121
גבולה	....	46
ליהוה	....	56
והיה	....	26
לאות	....	437
ולעד	....	110
ליהוה	....	56
צבאות	....	499
בארץ	....	293
מצרים	....	380
כי	....	30
יצעקו	....	276
אל	....	31
יהוה	....	26
מפני	....	180
לחצים	....	178
וישלח	....	354
להם	....	75
מושיע	....	426
ורב	....	208
והצילם	....	<u>181</u>
		5,449

Height of the Great Pyramid in
Pyramid Inches, to the original
summit platform _ _ _ _ _ _ _ _ 5,449

131

This identification of the Great Pyramid through gematria is startling. The words used to describe its location and purpose also tell us its height, 5,449.

The Great Pyramid has been one of the mysteries that has come down to us from our remote past. It was built over 4,000 years ago, and for most of that time it has held its secrets intact. Do we have a key that will help to unlock those secrets.

A key? Yes! Let's apply the *key,* מפתח, 528 – *the breaking forth of light,* כשחר, 528.

The Great Pyramid was once called the *Pyramid of Light,* or sometimes just *The Light.* This was because its polished white limestone casing reflected the sun's rays, giving it a brilliance that dazzled as the sun.

Photo courtesy Todd Alexander, Pyramid Productions, Inc.

Most of the beautiful white limestone casing have been stripped from the Pyramid centuries ago. The few remaining stones at its base give evidence of the size and quality of those huge stones.

Earth's orbit of the Sun, at 93 million miles, would have a mean diameter of 186 million miles. Dropping all the zeros, that distance stated in inches would be 1,178,496.

State the height of the Great Pyramid in feet, add the *key,* 528, and convert it to inches. The number is the same as Earth's orbit of the Sun, with the inclusion of a decimal point— 11,784.96.

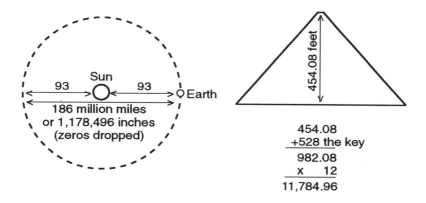

```
    454.08
  +528 the key
    982.08
  x     12
  11,784.96
```

This relationship of the Great Pyramid to light, by its height, is shown another way.

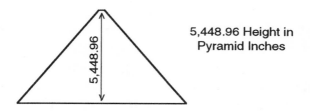

5,448.96 Height in Pyramid Inches

Divide its height by the Royal Egyptian Cubit—a unit used in the construction of the Great Pyramid, (1.72), and the result will be 3,168.

1.72 feet - Egyptian Royal Cubit

172 = *To divide*, בקע

5,448.96 ÷ 1.72 = 3,168
Lord Jesus Christ = 3,168

Jesus Christ, the Light of the World, is shown in the height of the Pyramid of Light.

The relationship of this Light to the Earth is also shown by the height of 5,448.96. Divide by the number value of the other way to spell *Jesus*, Ιησου, 688, and the result is 7.92, the number that represents Earth (Earth's diameter is 7,920 miles).

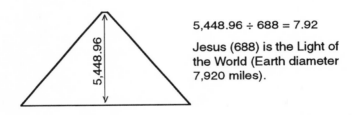

5,448.96 ÷ 688 = 7.92

Jesus (688) is the Light of the World (Earth diameter 7,920 miles).

In chapter 6 it was shown that a pentagon could be constructed on the Golden Proportion. A circle superscribed on a pentagon whose sides are 1 (Unity), will have a diameter of 1.72 (*To divide*, בקע = 172). If we divide Unity, as in the hydrogen molecule, the vesica that is formed has a width of .86, the number value of *Elohim*, אלהים.

THREE WITNESSES

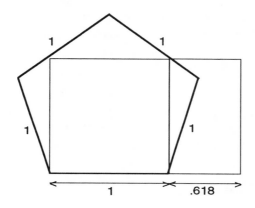

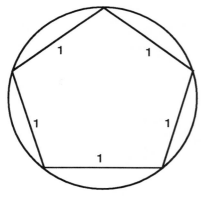

1	One side of pentagon
100	To divide, חצב
1.72	Diameter of circle
172	To divide, בקע
.86	Radius of circle
86	Dividing, מבדיל
.86	Width of vesica

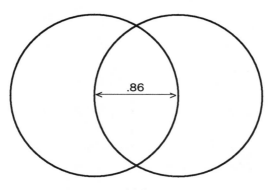

Using the *key,* 528, we considered each side of the pentagon 1 mile (5,280 feet), making the perimeter 316,800 inches. *Lord Jesus Christ,* 3,168, the Light of the World.

If we do the same thing with the vesica, the result is astounding! Multiply the width of the vesica by the *key,* then by 12 to convert it to inches. The width of the vesica in inches is precisely identical to the height of the Great Pyramid, from its socket level base to its summit platform.

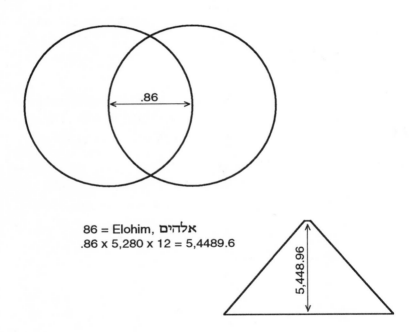

86 = Elohim, אלהים
.86 x 5,280 x 12 = 5,4489.6

5,448.96

If this were not designed by a Master Designer, it would be the world's most colossal coincidence! But it is not a coincidence. The Great Pyramid is the "witness" that both Jeremiah and Isaiah said was in the land of Egypt. It was there when they wrote their prophecies, and it is still there–a silent witness, bearing its evidence of a Master Architect. There's more!

Draw a square on the height of the Great Pyramid and it will have a perimeter of 21,795.84. Divide by *Jesus, Iησoυ,* 688, and the result is *Lord Jesus Christ,* 31.68.

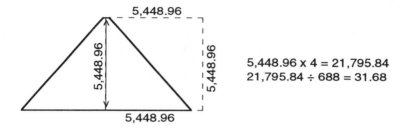

5,448.96 x 4 = 21,795.84
21,795.84 ÷ 688 = 31.68

Draw a circle on the height of the Great Pyramid and the circumference will again tell us of Jesus, the Light of the World.

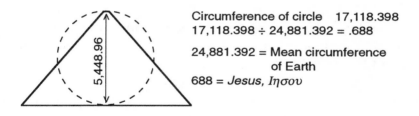

Circumference of circle   17,118.398
17,118.398 ÷ 24,881.392 = .688

24,881.392 = Mean circumference
of Earth
688 = *Jesus, Iησoυ*

The evidence that the Great Pyramid was indeed the "witness" Isaiah was referring to is overwhelming. It's relationship to the Earth and Moon are awesome.

Referring back to the concept of the Earth and Moon as a unit, orbiting the Sun, we placed the Moon tangent to the Earth to get their combined measures. Now let's draw a triangle on their centers. The diameter of the Earth will be the base of the triangle and its apex would be precisely at the center of the Moon. The triangle thus formed will be the exact proportions of the Great Pyramid, with a base angle of 51° 51´.

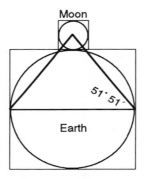

The Great Pyramid was built on the geometry of Earth and Moon. The perimeter of the base of this Earth-commensurate pyramid is 31,680 miles. It bears the signature of the Lord Jesus Christ. It is his witness.

The location of the Great Pyramid at the entrance of the Nile Delta is also part of the witness. If we traced a compass along the extremities of the Nile Delta, the point of the compass would be resting on the Great Pyramid. The Nile Delta, in its positional relationship to the Great Pyramid, forms a quadrant of a circle, with the Great Pyramid at its center, as was described by Isaiah. If we continued drawing the rest of the circle, it would have a diameter of 216 miles. The distance from the Great Pyramid to the northern-most tip of the delta is 108 miles–the radius of the circle.

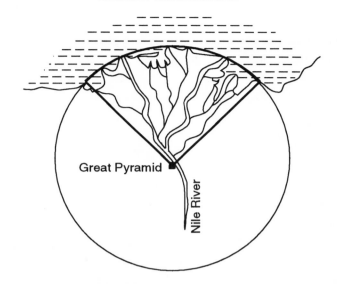

This is startling evidence of a Designer, for if we super-scribed a square on that circle, it would be precisely the same as a square superscribed on the Moon, divided by 10.

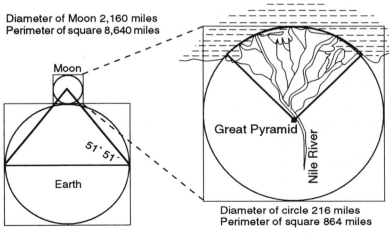

139

Is it a colossal coincidence, or the careful planning of a Master Designer? Even the supposed geographical and astronomical knowledge of the ancient builders could not have accomplished this one, for they could not control nor devise the shape and size of the Nile Delta. That required a Designer greater than man.

Again, if we apply the *key*, 528, some interesting numbers appear. The diameter multiplied by 5,280 will become 1,140,480 feet, which is 360 x 3,168. The square that we superscribed on the circle, multiplied by 5,280, will become 4,561,920 feet, or 144 x 3,168. The signature of the Designer was surely planted there.

The Great Pyramid is at the center of the circle. In fact, if the topstone, which was never lifted into place, were indeed on the Pyramid, it would be precisely at the center of the 216 mile diameter. Jesus referred to that missing stone, and used it as a symbol of himself. He called it *"The stone which the builders rejected,"* (Matt. 21:42). In the Greek text of the New Testament it is written as $\lambda \iota \theta o v$ $o v$ $\alpha \pi \epsilon \delta o \kappa \iota \mu \alpha \sigma \alpha v$ $o \iota$ $o \iota \kappa o \delta o \mu o v v \tau \epsilon \varsigma$, which adds to 2,160. The identification of the stone with its geographical location is amazing!

That topstone, bearing its identification number of 2,160, corresponds to the Moon with its diameter of 2,160 miles. The diagram of the square superscribed on the Moon also represents the Sun by its perimeter of 8,640 miles (solar number, 864). Thus the Pyramid of Light, whose topstone represents the *"Light of the World,"* (Jesus), corresponds to the *"two great lights,"* the Sun and Moon. And, as we know, the light of the Moon is really solar light reflected. It is fitting that the Hebrew word which means *"to make light,"* האיר, adds to 216.

The circle that can be drawn on the Nile Delta, with the Great Pyramid at its center becomes even more beautiful when we apply the "growth by division" principle to form a vesica.

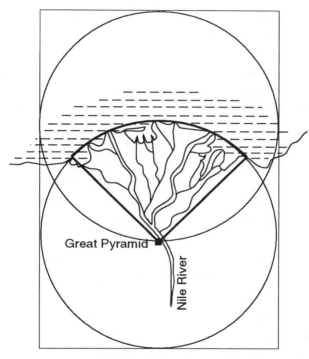

Width of vesica 108 miles
Perimeter of rectangle 1,080 miles

The width of the vesica is the 108 miles from the Great Pyramid to the northern tip of the delta. Apply the *key,* 528, and the width would be 570,240 feet (180 x 3,168), or 6,842,880 inches (2,160 x 3,168).

The 1 and the 8 are important. They are the numbers of beginning and new beginning–the numbers of the Creator and the work of creation, as shown on pages 101 and 102.

The precise location of the Great Pyramid is also shown by the true shape of the Earth.

Thus far I have been using the mean diameter of the Earth. However, in reality, the Earth is not a perfect sphere, but is flattened at the poles, and bulges slightly at the equator, due to the centrifugal force of its rotation. The ratio of its polar diameter to its equatorial diameter is 296:297. Based upon this unique proportion, the Great Pyramid describes its own location–its precise latitude. This remarkable fact was first discovered by Herbert L. Prout in 1933. It provides firm evidence that the Great Pyramid is indeed the "witness" that Jeremiah said was in the land of Egypt.

The proportion relates to the Great Pyramid by the angle of its descending (entrance) passage, which is 26.3°. This passage points directly north. A person standing at the bottom of the descending passage can see the pole star neatly framed by the entrance way. If we project an imaginary line out from the descending passage toward the pole star, it will intersect the axial line of Earth at precisely seven Earth-diameters away from the center of the Earth. If the Great Pyramid had been built even 100 feet from its true site, or if the passage angle were minutely different, this remarkable relationship would be lost.

The entrance passage becomes a pointer, pin-pointing its precise location on the face of the Earth. This is only possible because of the 296:297 ratio of Earth's polar diameter to its equatorial diameter. The gematria of those two numbers reveals the signature of the Designer.

296 *God,* צור

296 *Earth,* הארץ

296 *Only begotten* (the Son), μονογενη

296 *Son of man* (the name He assumed while he was the man, Jesus) υιος του ανθρωπου

297 *North* (the direction of the entrance passage), מזרים

297 *A Branch of Righteousness* (prophetic name of Jesus), צמח נדקה (Jer. 33:15)

Thus far I have referred to the height of the Great Pyramid, measuring from its socket level base up to its summit platform—a height of 5,448.960 Pyramid inches (454 feet). However, had its magnificent topstone ever been placed upon its summit, it would have measured 485 feet to its apex. There is no evidence that the topstone was ever placed. It would have been gigantic—about 31 feet high and 48 feet wide.

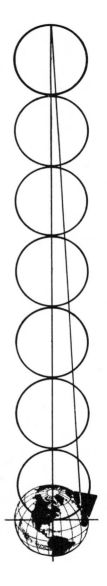

The relationship of the topstone to the Pyramid's square base is as the relationship of the Sun to the Earth, the base representing Earth's orbit around the Sun.

This chief cornerstone of the entire structure bears the solar number in gematria. *Cornerstone, γωνια,* adds to 864, the solar number (Sun's diameter is 864,000 miles). It represents the Sun, and the Sun represents God; thus *God, Θεων,* has a number value of 864.

The total height of 485 feet for the Pyramid of Light beautifully illustrates the statement made by the prophet Isaiah, *"The Lord shall be unto you an everlasting light,"* (Isaiah 60:19). Its letter-numbers add to 485. The number 485 is also the gematria for *"There is no Rock like our God,"* (I Sam. 2:2), ואין צור כאלהינו. That He should be called a Rock in this statement, whose number value is the same as the height of the Great Pyramid, is most significant, for that structure is the greatest pile of rocks known to man.

The top cornerstone, bearing the solar number, 864, not only represents the Creator (*God, Θεων,* 864), and light, it also represents the foundation of creation—the beginning. The geometry and gematria are amazing.

The Sun's diameter is 864,000 miles. A square inscribed within a circle whose diameter is 864 will have sides of 611.

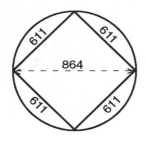

Diameter of circle	864
One side of square	611
Perimeter of square	2,444

864 = Solar number

864 *God, Θεων*

864 *Cornerstone, γωνια*

611 *Foundation,* אשיש

611 *A tried stone, a precious cornerstone* (prophetic of Jesus), בחן אבן יקר פנה אבן, (Isaiah 28:16)

2444 *The beginning of creation, αρχης κτισεως,* (II Pet. 3:4)

2444 *The Lord your God, Κυριος ο Θεος υμων,* (Acts. 4:22)

This relationship of the Sun to the Creator and the beginning of creation, is also the same relationship of light to the topstone of the Pyramid. That topstone was referred to in Psalm 118:22 and it was called *"The head of the corner."* It's Hebrew letter-numbers add to 666.

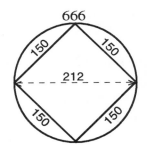

Circumference of circle	666
Diameter of circle	212
One side of square	150
Permieter of square	600

666 *The head of the corner,* לראש פנה, (Psalm 118:22)

666 *Let there be lights,* יהי מארת, (Genesis 1:14)

212 (2120) *Light, φωτισμος*

212 *Light,* אורה

212 *To shine* (brightness), זהר

150   (1500) *Light,* φως

600   *World (kosmos,* the created order), κοσμος

If we were to use the precise proportions of this chief cornerstone of the Pyramid in a circle, as the above square is in the circle, it tells the story of light, and of Jesus, the Light of the World, and the beautiful Golden Proportion. The design is based upon the mean orbit of the Earth around the Sun, 186 million miles.

Diameter of inner circle	186
Diameter of outer circle	236.8
Circumference of inner circle	584.336
Circumference of outer circle	744
Sides of upright "cornerstone"	301
Sides of both "cornerstones"	602
Height of "cornerstone"	118.4

186   *Jehovah is my Rock,* סלע יהוה, (Psalm 18:2)

186   *His work* (creation), פעלו, (Psalm 111:3)

186   *Golgotha* (place of Jesus' death), Γολγοθα

186   *The beginning of the world,* מעולם

2368   *Jesus Christ,* Ιησους Χριστος

2368   *The God of gods,* ο Θεος των θεων

5840   *God and Father of our Lord Jesus Christ,*
Θεος και πατηρ του Κυριου ημων Ιησου Χριστου
(I Peter. 1:3)

744   *Two great lights* (Sun and Moon), המאורת הגדלים

THREE WITNESSES

301	*He is the Rock,* הצור, (Deut. 32:4)
301	*Calvary* (place of Jesus' death), κρανιον
301	*Moon,* σεληνη
301	*Foundation,* אש
602	*Godhead* (divinity), Θειοτης
1184	*Chief cornerstone,* ακρογωνιαιον
1184	*In a different form* (Jesus, after his resurrection appeared "in a different form" to the two disciples on the road to Emmaus), εν ετερα μορφη, (Mark 16:12)

This amazing design, based upon the proportion of the topstone of the Great Pyramid and the distance that light travels from the Sun to Earth, is made even more awesome by its Golden Proportion.

Yes, not only the topstone, but the whole Pyramid is a demonstration of the beautiful Golden Proportion by the same relationship (base to sides).

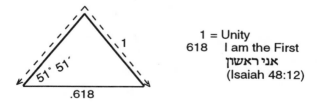

1 = Unity
618   I am the First
אני ראשון
(Isaiah 48:12)

It is the union, or marriage, of the pentagon and the heptagon. A 5-pointed star is constructed on the Golden Proportion, and the famous "Pyramid angle" (base to apex), as well

147

as the passage angle, are the two primary angles in the 7-pointed star.

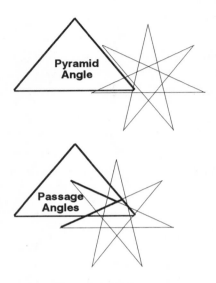

This stone witness in the land of Egypt has been a silent testimony to the Creator and to His creation for more than 4,000 years. The stones were quarried and lifted into place by man, but its design bears the signature of the Great Designer.

From its base to its summit platform, there are 203 courses of masonry. Its completion, in preparation for the placing of the topstone, bears the signature of the Creator, for the number value for *Creator,* ברא, is 203. What a witness!

Jeremiah said that the second witness would be in Israel. What was there in Israel in Jeremiah's day, built by the hands of men, that would be a witness of a Beginner–a Creator? It would need to be a place that holds his signature. Again we find it is not only the structure, but also the *place* where it is built, that is the "sign and witness." And by its geometry and gematria it is inseparably linked to the "sign and witness" in Egypt.

This witness in Israel was Solomon's Temple, built on the hill that had come to be known as the meeting place between God and man. That hill was sometimes called the Foundation, and sometimes simply the Rock.

History first tells us of that hill (then called Moriah) during the time of Abraham. It was there that Abraham's God had instructed him to perform a sacrifice–a sacrifice that pictured, or illustrated, the sacrifice that God, himself, would make by offering His only begotten Son as man's Redeemer. Both offerings were made on the same hill–Mount Moriah. (Abraham's son, however, did not actually die, because God provided a ram to be offered in his stead.)

Long after the time of Abraham, one of his descendants, King Solomon, built a temple there. This hill had been chosen for the Temple site because it had long been regarded as the most sacred spot on Earth–the meeting place between God and men.

In the year 586 B.C., Babylon's king Nebuchadnezzar laid siege to Jerusalem and burned the Temple. The site lay desolate until 70 years later when some of the Israelites, under the leadership of Zerubbabel, built another temple there. In 21 B.C., Herod the Great, who ruled the land of Judea under Caesar Augustus of Rome, built a third temple on the ruins of the second one. This beautiful temple of Herod was destroyed by the army of Titus in A.D. 70–Rome's siege of Jerusalem. Till today, the only thing left is a portion of a retaining wall, now known as the Western Wall. But the site remains sacred to Israelites as well as Christians.[1]

The Rock on which Abraham offered his typical sacrifice has been the foundation for each of the structures that had been built upon it. Thus it has come to be known as the Rock, or the Foundation.

Calvary, Golgotha—the place where Jesus was crucified, is part of that same hill of Moriah. Today, due to construction and excavation, they appear to be separate hills, but in Abraham's day it was one. Abraham named it Jehovah-jireh—"The Mount of the Lord."

$$Jehovah, \text{יהוה} = 26$$
$$jireh, \text{יראה} = 216$$

The two names by which it has come to be known today are Calvary and Golgotha. The gematria for these two names reveals the beautiful Golden Proportion, shown in the diagram of the Great Pyramid's relationship to Earth's distance from the Sun.

186   *Golgotha, Γολγοθα*
301   *Calvary, κρανιον*

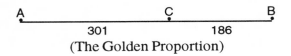

(The Golden Proportion)

---

1   Above this retaining wall now stands the Mosque of Omar, built in A.D. 738.

186
(186 million miles)

Jehovah, יהוה
$ה^2 + ו^2 + ה^2 + י^2 = 186$

A square with sides of 301 will have a perimeter of 1,204, which is the gematria for *The Holy Mount at Jerusalem,* בהר הקדש בירושלם, (Isaiah 27:13).

A square with sides of 186 will have a perimeter of 744, which is the gematria for *Zion at Jerusalem,* ציון בירושלם, (Isaiah 30:19). The way the numbers are interwoven into the design makes the identification unmistakable. The Temple and its Holy Mount are the witness that Jeremiah said was in the land of Israel.

The Temple was divided into two principal rooms, called the Holy, and Most Holy. The Holy was rectangular, measuring 20 cubits by 40 cubits, while the Most Holy was a large square room, measuring 20 cubits by 20 cubits.

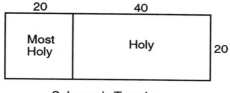

Solomon's Temple

But what was the length of the cubit? The Hebrew scriptures give us a clue.

Now these are the things wherein Solomon was instructed for the building of the house of God. The length by cubits after the first measure was threescore cubits and the breadth twenty cubits. (II Chronicles 3:3)

The "first measure" was the old measure that had been handed down from ancient Sumer. It was a cubit of 19.8 inches. Through the years, Israel had come to use a longer cubit, the Egyptian Royal Cubit. However, the chronicler made it clear that it was the old cubit that was to be used for the construction of the Temple.[1]

The base perimeter of the Temple was 160 cubits of the "first measure," – 19.8 inches – which would be 264 feet, or 3,168 inches. It bore the signature of the Designer, the *Lord Jesus Christ, Κυριος Ιησους Χριστος,* whose number is 3,168.

The inner sanctuary of the Temple was a square room called the Holy of Holies, or Most Holy. Its letter-numbers add to 864, both in Hebrew and in Greek. It is the solar number, the number of *life, ζωην,* 864; the number of *God, Θεων,* 864; and the number of the topstone of the Pyramid, *cornerstone, γωνια,* 864. The fact that it bears the same number in both Hebrew and Greek tells us the number was intentional and important. It is the number that represents the source of all life.

The Holy of Holies was the meeting place between God and men. It measured 20 cubits on each side, making a perim-

---

1 The length of the Temple cubit is given as 19.8 inches in the *Encyclopedia Judiaca,* Keter Publishing House, Jerusalem, 1972, p. 947.

eter of 80 cubits. Converted to feet it would be 132 – the number that appears to be basic to creation. We saw 132 in the protons of the 6 molecules of carbon dioxide in the process of photosynthesis. The number was used again in the aggregate wave lengths of the 6 colors of white light; and the word *white,* in Hebrew, is 132. It is the number basic to music, being the number of vibrations per second in C below Middle C. It is the side of a Golden Rectangle whose inscribed spiral bears the number of the *Lord Jesus Christ,* 3,168. It is intrinsic to the creation of man, *anthropos,* 132. It describes man as having been made in the likeness of his Creator–*"He made him in the likeness of God,"* 1,320. It is the number that describes the first act of creation, the dividing of Unity–*God divided,* 132. The sum and the product of its digits is the basic 6, the first perfect number. It can all be summed up in the Greek word $\iota\alpha o\mu\alpha\iota$, *to make whole,* 132.

The geometry of the floor plan of the Holy of Holies not only bears the signature of the Creator, its multiples bear the sacred numbers of creation.

132 x 2 = 264

264   *Truth,* $\alpha\lambda\eta\theta\epsilon\iota\alpha\varsigma$

2640   *The Light* (Jesus), $\tau o\upsilon\ \phi\omega\tau o\varsigma$

132 x 3 = 396

3960 miles - radius of Earth

3960   *Jehovah-shalom* (Jehovah is peace)

396   *The name of Jehovah,* לשם יהוה

132 x 4 = 528

528   *The Key,* מפתח

528   *The breaking forth of light,* כשחר

132 x 6 = 792

7920 miles - diameter of Earth

792   *Jehovah, the Maker of the heavens,* יהוה עשה שמים

132 x 8 = 1,056

1,056   *I form the light, I create darkness,* יוצר אור ובורא חשך

132 x 16 = 2,112

2,112   *A virgin shall conceive and bear a son, and shall call his name Immanuel,*

(Isa. 7:14) העלמה הרה וילדת בן וקראת שמו עמנו אל

2,112   *Glory of the Lord,* δοξης του κυριου

132 x 24 = 3,168

31,680 miles - a square enclosing Earth

3,168   *Lord Jesus Christ, Κυριος Ιησους Χριστος*

3,168   *Mediator between God and man,*
       μεσιτης Θεου και ανθρωπων (I Tim. 2:5)

The Holy of Holies, bearing its solar number 864, the number of *life,* has sides of 20 cubits each—a square. Super-scribe a circle on that square and it bears the number for *Jesus, Ιησους,* 888, the life giver.

Circumference 88.8 cubits

Immediately outside the Temple, in the courtyard, Solomon made a large receptacle for water. It was called the Molten Sea. This sea was supported on the backs of 12 identical oxen, cast in bronze.

THREE WITNESSES

**The Molten Sea
supported by 12 oxen**

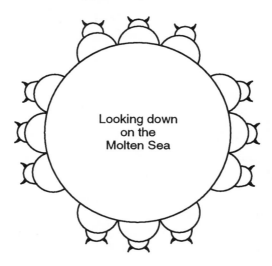

Looking down
on the
Molten Sea

He also made a Molten Sea of ten cubits from brim to brim, round in compass.... It stood upon twelve oxen, three looking toward the north, three looking toward the west, three looking toward the south, and three looking toward the east. The sea was set above them, and all their hinder parts were inward. (II Chron. 4:2-4)

A square superscribed on the circle of the Molten Sea would have a perimeter of 792 inches–the Earth number (7,920 miles).

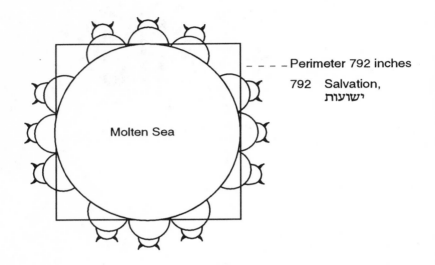

— — — — Perimeter 792 inches

792 Salvation, ישועות

Molten Sea

The hill, Golgotha (Calvary), where Jesus died, was the same hill where the Molten Sea had been placed, outside the Temple. That the Molten Sea should represent salvation is most fitting. The relationship of the gematria for *Golgotha,* 186, to *Calvary,* 301, is the Golden Proportion. It is the basis of the pentagram–the 5-pointed star.

The Molten Sea incorporates within its design the heptagram–the 7-pointed star. We saw both the pentagram and the heptagram demonstrated by the Great Pyramid, the "witness" in Egypt. Now we see them both demonstrated in the Temple, the "witness" in the land of Israel.

The 12 oxen supporting the Molten Sea faced in the

directions of the four cardinal compass points, with 3 on each side. On the basis of that design, a heptagram can be drawn.

The Molten Sea and the heptagram

The number 7 is the number of the *Temple,* ההיכל, 70. It is the number of *purity,* αγνεια, 70, represented by the water in the Molten Sea. It is the number for the *Mercy Seat,* כפרת, 700, which was in the Holy of Holies. Thus the 7-pointed star is a design that has to do with salvation. Seven precedes 8, just as the 7 notes of the diatonic scale lead to the 8th, which is the 1st of the next series. 8 is the number of a new beginning. Salvation must precede the new beginning.

When we use the *key,* 528, to unlock this "witness" in the land of Israel, it tells us about the One who provided the means of our salvation.

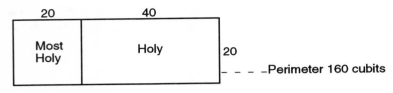

Solomon's Temple

$$528 \div 160 = 3.3$$
$$160 \div 528 = .303$$

330   *Holy and just One* (Jesus), αγιον και δικαιον, (Acts 3:14)

3030   *The Son of Man* (Jesus), ο υιος του ανθρωπου, (John 3:13)

330   *To make atonement,* לכפר

Jesus was 33 years old when he hung on the cross on Calvary in A.D. 33. It was the same hill where Abraham had offered his son as a sacrifice. Now God was offering His Son, to atone for man, and bring salvation.

The water in the Molten Sea pictured salvation and life. Isaiah prophesied *"With joy shall you draw water out of the wells of salvation,"* (Isaiah. 12:3). The Hebrew word for *"draw water,"* שאב, bears the number 303.

The "witness" in the land of Israel does indeed hold the signature of its Architect–the Architect of the hill, as well as the structure built upon it. It was the meeting place between God and men, the place where atonement was made.

The third "witness" of which Jeremiah spoke was *"among other men."* He was not specific. It could possibly be any-where in the world. Where do we look? Is there only one among other men, or are there many? We know that it would be something that was in existence in Jeremiah's day. Other than that, he gave us no clues.

The ancient records, as well as legends, tell that Jeremiah, some years after writing his prophecy, sailed to the islands that we now call the British Isles. It is a logical place to look for the third "witness."

The first two witnesses related to circles, squares, rectangles and triangles. Is there a place in the British Isles that relates to these geometric designs? Yes, there is a spot where the rising and setting of the Sun and Moon trace a rectangle. It is the only land area on Earth where this happens. (Its corresponding location in the southern hemisphere is on the ocean.) On this strategic geographical location, stands the 4,000-year old configuration of stones, known as Stonehenge.

This is an artist's conception of Stonehenge as it was originally built. It probably shows more stones in the Bluestone Circle than originally existed, but it shows the beautiful symmetry of its construction.

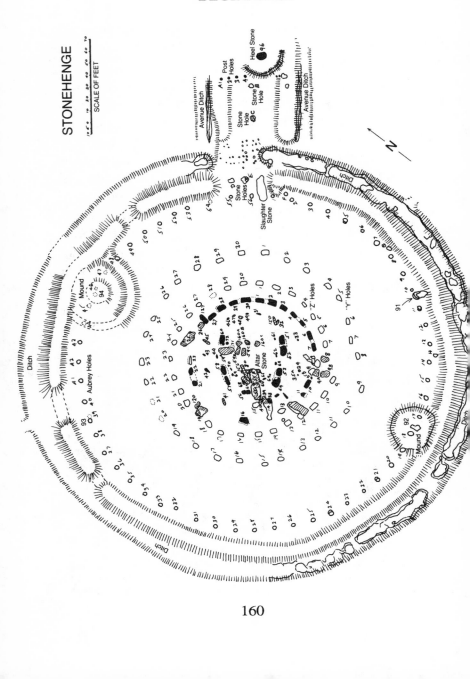

STONEHENGE

SCALE OF FEET

THREE WITNESSES

Stonehenge is nearly as old as the Great Pyramid, and in all the ages since its construction, men have built nothing comparable to it. And, like the Great Pyramid, the solutions to the mystery that surrounds it have been sincerely sought by scientists, theologians, architects and historians.

Stonehenge is a series of concentric circles, some of which were made of stones and some were made of earth. Some were holes dug in the ground. Those holes formed a large circle. They were discovered in 1666 by John Aubrey, thus they have been named the Aubrey Circle. On the circumference of that circle (999 feet), can be found 4 large unhewn stones, called Station Stones, placed to form a rectangle. The Station Stone Rectangle precisely traces the risings and settings of the Sun and Moon.

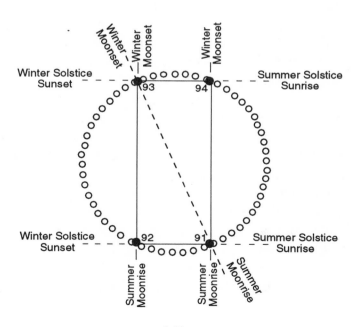

The dimensions of the rectangle are startling. The long side is 3,168 inches, bearing the signature of the Designer. The perimeter is precisely the length of one side of the Great Pyramid at its base that rests on the natural bedrock, namely .144 of a mile.

The diagonal of the rectangle measures 3,456 inches, correspoding to a square superscribed on the Sun (3,456,000 miles). But the most remarkable thing about the Station Stone Rectangle is that it points directly to the Great Pyramid. If you were to begin walking from Station Stone 93 to Station Stone 91 (the only two remaining today), and keep walking in that precise direction, eventually you would bump into the Great Pyramid. That Station Stone diagonal is, in fact, the arc of a Great Circle which touches both Stonehenge and the Great Pyramid.

Its length, 3,456 inches, relating to the Sun, points directly to the Pyramid of Light. Surely Stonehenge is the "witness" for which we are searching—the one that Jeremiah said was *"among other men."*

Within the Aubrey Circle of holes, stands a circle of huge monoliths, joined together by large stone lintels. It has been named the Sarsen Circle, because all of its stones are of sarsen. The mean circumference of the Sarsen Circle is 316.8 feet, bearing the signature of the Designer.

Immediately within the Sarsen Circle stands a ring of smaller stones which has been named the Bluestone Circle. It has a diameter of 79.2 feet, showing its relationship to the Earth, whose diameter is 7,920 miles.

The inmost ring of bluestones is open-ended, looking sort of like a horseshoe. Thus it has been named the Bluestone Horseshoe. It has a diameter of 39.6 feet, being exactly half

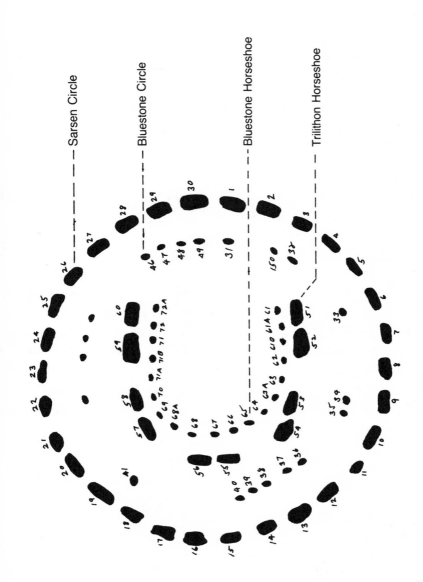

the size of the Bluestone Circle.

If a triangle or a hexagon were drawn within the Blue-stone Circle, the Bluestone Horseshoe would exactly fit within it.

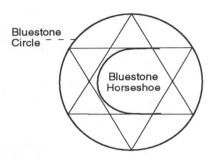

A square superscribed on the Bluestone Circle will have a perimeter of 316.8 feet, just like a square superscribed on the Earth will have a perimeter of 31,680 miles. The Sarsen Circle, with its mean circumference of 316.8 feet, reshaped as a square, would exactly fit over the Bluestone Circle. The Earth-Moon-Pyramid model is also the model for Stonehenge.

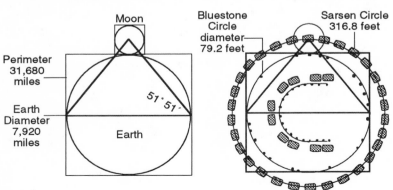

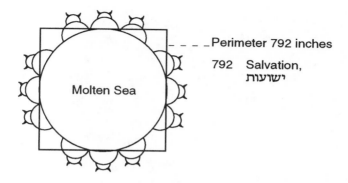

Perimeter 792 inches

792   Salvation,
ישועות

The function of Stonehenge was the tracking of the apparent movements of the Sun and Moon in relation to Earth. At the summer solstice, the longest day of the year, the Sun is at its most northern extreme. Before it begins southward, it appears to pause at this most northern extremity of its swing.

If we were standing in the center of Stonehenge on the morning of summer solstice, we would see the Sun make its appearance slightly to the left of the Heelstone–a large unhewn monolith that stands 256 feet from the center where we are standing. Because the Sun is at its most northern extreme, it moves at a narrow angle toward the south as it rises, and momentarily hides behind the Heelstone. Then it appears to burst forth from the top of the Heelstone as a golden crown.

Due to a phenomenon known as the precession of the equinoxes, the Sun slips back slightly every year, making its appearance further south. However, through 4,000 years, the Sun has never separated from the Heelstone at the solstice sunrise. Today it still crowns that ancient stone with its golden glory.

Thus, even though the relationship of Sun to Earth

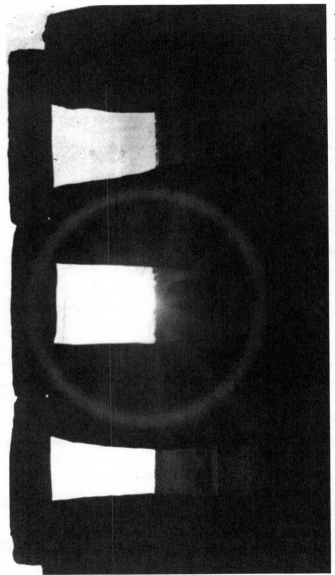

More than a million sunrises have cast their warmth over the mute stones of Stonehenge, and today, the sun at the summer solstice still rises over the Heelstone, appearing as a golden crown upon its ancient head.

changes slightly, the angle of sunrise is permanently marked by the position of the Heelstone. It is 51° 51′ from north. The same angle as the Great Pyramid from base to apex, and the same angle as the triangle drawn on the centers of Earth and Moon.

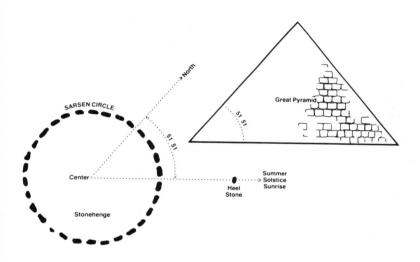

Surrounding the circle of 56 holes (the Aubrey Circle), is an earth bank that was once about 6 feet high. As well as serving as an enclosure for the site, it also formed an artificial horizon for viewing the risings and settings of the Sun and Moon. It is fitting that the diameter of this bank, at its crest, was 318 feet, for the word *Sun, ηλιος,* has a number value of 318; while the radius was .0301 of a mile, and 301 is the number value for the *Moon, σελﻻνη.*

The bank which forms the horizon for viewing the Sun and Moon has a circumference of 999 feet. It relates to the beginning of creation: *"In the beginning God,"* בראשית אלהים,

999, (Genesis 1:1). The Sun could be viewed, rising over the bank, and filling the world with the glory of its light. Because the Sun represents God, the source of light and life, the 999 feet of the circular horizon speaks of the *"Glory of God,"* δοξαν Θεω, which adds to 999.

It has been demonstrated that the 7-pointed star relates to the first two "witnesses." Combining the Earth-Moon-Pyramid-Stonehenge diagram with the Molten Sea, a 7-pointed star can be drawn on the ground plan of Stonehenge. When we do this it becomes apparent that the Architect designed the circles on the geometry of the heptagram. This was observed by John Ivimy.[1]

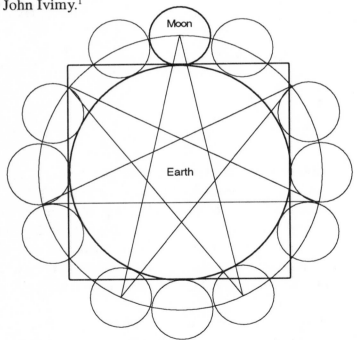

---

1 John Ivimy, *The Sphinx and the Megaliths,* Turnstone, 1974.

THREE WITNESSES

The point of intersection of the arms of the star precisely mark the outer circumference of the Sarsen Circle.

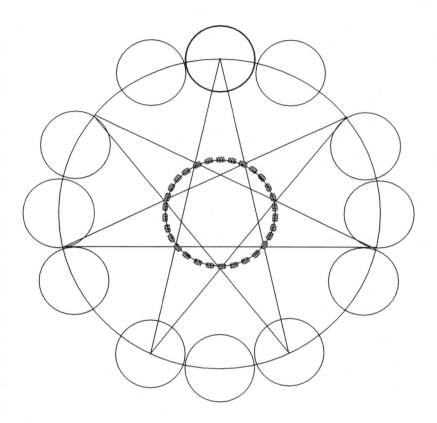

If this were overlaid with another 7-pointed star, making 14 points, the intersecting lines would precisely mark the outer circumference of the Bluestone Circle. In its center will be found the Trilithon and Bluestone Horseshoes, perfectly enclosed by the inner face of the double heptagram. It is no coincidence!

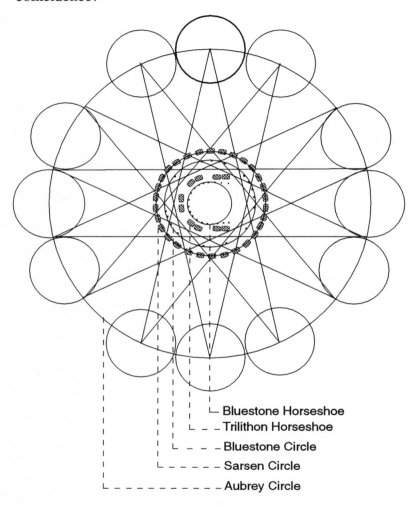

Bluestone Horseshoe
Trilithon Horseshoe
Bluestone Circle
Sarsen Circle
Aubrey Circle

THREE WITNESSES

The Aubrey Circle is a ring of 56 holes. The arc between each point of the heptagram contains 8 of these holes

The relation of the 7-pointed star to a circle was shown by the action of sound frequencies (see page 126), and it is shown in each of the three witnesses.[1] Just as in music, the completion of 7 notes brings us back again to the same note, but an octave higher—the eighth becoming the first of the next series—so at Stonehenge, the 56 holes of the Aubrey Circle show the relationship of 7 to 8. Seven is completion (salvation), and 8 is a new beginning.

What is the new beginning?

---

1 An in-depth study of each of the three witnesses is available from Bonnie Gaunt, 510 Golf Avenue, Jackson, Michigan 49203.
Stonehenge...a closer look   ($10.00)
The Magnificent Numbers of the Great Pyramid and Stonehenge ($10.00)
The Stones Cry Out   ($7.00)
Stonehenge and the Great Pyramid: Window on the Universe   ($10.00)

9
A New Beginning

This book is about beginnings. There is a Hebrew word that embodies not only the concept of beginning, but it also includes the idea of that which has no beginning–eternity. The word is *kedem,* קדם. It adds to 144. Although *kedem* is used as a root for *beginning,* or *origin,* it strangely carries the thought of no beginning nor ending–eternal, everlasting. The meaning of the word is best represented by a circle, which, of course, has no beginning nor ending point. The word *circle,* in Hebrew is חוג, and it multiplies to 144.

In chapter 1 the circle, representing the *El* was illustrated by the hydrogen atom, with its characteristic 1 at its nucleus, being orbited by its 1 electron, forming a wave bubble, or circle around the proton.

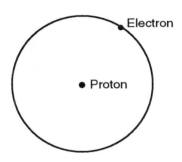

Thus the number 144 (12²) was the number of *El* from the *beginning* or from *eternity*. His very nature bears the number 144 in Greek—*Theion, Θειον, divine nature,* adds to 144.

The first act of creation was the dividing of Unity, as is illustrated by the hydrogen molecule. It is the principle of growth by division.

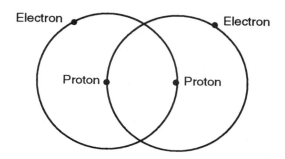

The Hebrew words for *God divided* are יבדל אלהים, and they add to 132, which has been found to be basic to all creation; and they multiply to 144, the number of *beginning* and *eternity.*

In Greek, the words *God* and *Create* bear numbers that are anagrams of each other.

Create, επoιησεv	428
God, Θεoς	-284
	144

The creation of man in the image of God also carries the number 144.

1440   *Let us make man in our image, after our likeness and let him rule.* נעשה אדם בצלמנו כדמותנו וירדו (Gen. 1:26)

173

But man (*anthropos, ανθρωποις,* 1320) fell from that position of rulership in divine likeness. The first man, Adam, fell because of disobedience, and needed a redeemer to regain his lost life-rights and position of divine likeness and rulership.

The prophet Isaiah foretold the coming of that Redeemer. He said:

> *For unto us a child is born, and unto us a Son is given: and the government shall be upon His shoulder; and His name shall be called Wonderful, Counsellor, the Mighty God, the Everlasting Father, the Prince of Peace. Of the increase of His government and peace there shall be no end; upon the throne of David, and upon his kingdom, to order it, and to establish it with judgment and with justice from henceforth even forever.* (Isaiah 9:6,7)

That child, who was prophesied to be born, and to grow up to be a ruler of peace, bore the number 144.

> 144 (by multiplication) *A child is born*
> 88 (by addition) *A child is born*
> ילד ילד

In the fulfillment of Isaiah's prophecy, the child was born. It was the promise and the surety of a new beginning. The child was to bring salvation to a dying human race, and the eventual restoration of man to the image and likeness of his Creator—a ruler.

Just as the place of the beginning, Eden, bore the number of wholeness, a double 9, so the place of new beginning also bore a double 9.

99   *Garden of the Lord* (Eden),
      כגן יהוה (Genesis 13:10)
      The place of beginning

99   *Bethlehem, Βηθλεεμ*
      The place of new beginning

The little town of Bethlehem, bearing its number 99, rested on 31.68° N latitude. The child that was born became the *Lord Jesus Christ, Κυριος Ιησους Χριστος,* who bore the number 3,168.

The numbers 1 and 8 represent beginning and new beginning, respectively. The Hebrew word for *beginning,* אך, adds to 8. *Jesus, Ιησους,* the promise of a new beginning, bore the number 888. The circumstances of his conception and birth also bear the number 8.

8 x 888   *The power of the Most High will overshadow you, and for that reason the holy offspring will be called the Son of God. δυναμις υψιστου επισκιασει σοι διο και το γεννωμενον αγιον κληθησεται υιος Θεου,* (Luke 1:35)

8,880   *Behold, a virgin shall conceive and bear a Son, and shall call his name Emmanuel, which being interpreted is, God with us. ιδου η παρθενος εν γαστρι εξει και τεξεται υιον και καλεσουσιν ονομα αυτου Εμμανουηλ ο εστιν μεθερμηνευομενον μεθ ημων Θεος,* (Matt. 1:23).

8 x 888   *When the time had come, God sent forth his Son, born of a woman. οτε ηλθεν πληρωμα χρονου εξαπεστειλεν Θεος τον υιον αυτου γενομενον εκ γυναικος.* (Gal. 4:4)

888   *Jesus, Ιησους*

888   *Salvation of our God,* ישועת אלהינו, (Isaiah 52:10)

888   *As a lamb to the slaughter he was led, and as a ewe before her shearers,* כשה לטבח יובל וכרחל לפני גזזיה, (Isaiah 53:7)

8,888   *He must reign until he has put all enemies under His feet. δει γαρ αυτον βασιλευειν αχρι ου θη παντας τους εχθρους υπο τους ποδας αυτου,* (I Cor. 15:25)

Jesus said, *"I am the Alpha and Omega."* He was referring to himself as the first and last letters of the Greek alphabet, which are 1 and 800 – the 1 and 8 represents the beginning and the new beginning. *"Alpha and Omega,"* Αλφα και Ωμεγα, when multiplied, becomes 144 (zeros dropped).

The *key,* κλειδα, when multiplied, becomes 12, and $12^2 = 144$. The number 12 is basic to the beginning and the new beginning.

12   *The key* (multiplied), *κλειδα*

74   *Foundation,* יסד

740 *Creation, κτισις*

740 *Circle, κυκλος*

74   *Eternity,* עד

74 + 12 = 86, *Elohim* (beginning)

74 x 12 = 888, *Jesus* (new beginning)

The Hebrew word for *circle,* חוג, multiplies to 144. Thus the Beginner (*Elohim,* 86), and the New Beginner (*Jesus,* 888) are multiples of 12 (the *key,* 12); and they are represented by a *circle* (144), the symbol of *eternity* (144). It is profound! Yet its simplicity is obvious and beautiful.

A NEW BEGINNING

There is a story making the rounds today (whether true or fabricated, I know not) about a computer programmer who put the entire New Testament into his computer, then asked the computer, "Why did Jesus come to Earth?" The computer, not having a doctrine, could answer only on the basis of input. It answered, "To establish a kingdom."

The underlying concept in all of His teachings, parables, miracles and lessons was the Kingdom of God. It was the New Beginning for which he came to Earth.

In reality, the New Beginning is the restoration of the first beginning. Genesis 1:1 starts with *"In the beginning God (Elohim)."* The Hebrew words add to 999, showing the wholeness and completeness of the realm of Elohim. His realm is his kingdom—it always was, still is, and always will be. *"In the beginning God,"* multiplies to 2,880 (zeros dropped). The *"Kingdom of heaven,"* $\beta\alpha\sigma\iota\lambda\epsilon\iota\alpha$ $\tau\omega\nu$ $\sigma\nu\rho\alpha\nu\omega\nu$, adds to 2,880 ($2 \times 12^2$). A square with sides of 288 will have a perimeter of 1,152. *"In the beginning God created,"* multiplies to 1,152 (zeros dropped). The *"Kingdom of God,"* $\tau\eta\nu$ $\beta\alpha\sigma\iota\lambda\epsilon\iota\alpha\nu$ $\Theta\epsilon\sigma\upsilon$, adds to 1,152. The *New Jerusalem,* the vision of that kingdom given to John, adds to 1,152. They are not random numbers—they tell a beautiful story.

$2 \times 144 = 288$

288   *Creator,* $\kappa\tau\iota\sigma\tau\eta$ (multiplied)

288   *Heaven is my throne,* השמים כסאי, (Isa. 66:1) (multiplied)

288(0) *In the beginning God* (multiplied)

288(0) *Kingdom of heaven* (added)

288   *Restorer,* משובב (Isa. 52:12) (multiplied)

8 x 144 = 1,152

1,152 *In the beginning God created* (multiplied)

1,152 *Thy kingdom,* מלכ ותך (Psalm 45:6) (multiplied)

1,152 *Kingdom of God* (added)

1,152 *New Jerusalem* (added)

144 *A Kingdom,* מלכו (multiplied)

144 *God reigns,* מלך אלהים (Psa. 47:8) (multiplied)

The *key* (multiplied), 12, is thus found to be that which unlocks the Kingdom of God.

When God *(Elohim)* made man *(anthropos,* 1320), and placed him in the Garden of Eden, *"He made him in the likeness of God,"* (1320). Man was to be ruler–*"Let him have dominion."* The original purity of man, in the likeness of his Creator, is represented in the number 132 (11 x 12), which we have seen is basic to all life on Earth. A purity that was lost. The promise that Isaiah recorded told of a child that would be born–a child that would grow to become an everlasting ruler, one who would rule in righteousness and peace. While the child was yet unborn, it bore the number 132, for *"the fruit of thy womb,"* (Jesus), adds to 1320 *(καρπος της κοιλιας).*

Part of Isaiah's prophecy said *"The government shall be upon His shoulder."* The governments that have been upon man's shoulder have all been corrupt. King Nebuchadnezzar of ancient Babylon was given a vision of those governments in the form of a strange image, whose head was made of gold, arms and breast of silver, abdomen and thighs of bronze, legs of iron and feet of iron and clay. He did not understand the vision, but Daniel told him that it represented all the governments of Earth. The vision concluded with a stone, strangely cut from the mountain, which hurled itself at the toes of the image, causing the whole image to crumble—so much so that the wind blew it all away. Then that little stone began to grow. It grew larger and larger, and soon it filled the whole Earth. As Daniel interpreted the vision for Nebuchadnezzar, he described the stone:

> And in the days of these kings (man's governments) shall the God of heaven set up a kingdom which shall never be destroyed. And the kingdom shall not be left to other people, but it shall break in pieces and consume all these kingdoms, and it shall stand forever. (Daniel 2:44)

The *"stone cut out of the mountain,"* מטורא אתגזרת אבן, adds to 1320. It is the kernel or nucleus of the Kingdom of God, and it bears the number 132. That stone was the child whom Isaiah prophesied would grow to become the Prince of Peace in a kingdom which would stand forever. That kingdom in its complete establishment, includes heaven (God's realm) and Earth (man's realm). It bears the number 132.

132   *The Kingdom is Jehovah's,*
יהוה המלוכה, (Psalm 22:28)

In that Kingdom man (*anthropos,* 1320) will once again be *"made whole,"* ιαομαι, 132.

Isaiah saw that New Beginning. He described it thus:

> For as the new heavens and new earth, which I will make, shall remain before me, saith the Lord, so shall your seed and your name remain. And it shall come to pass, that from one new moon to another, and from one sabbath to another, shall all flesh come to worship before me, saith the Lord. (Isaiah 66:22, 23)

The *"new heavens and new earth,"* השמים החדשים והארץ, multiplies to 248,832 (zeros dropped). By the rules of gematria it is the same as the mean circumference of Earth, which is 248,831.392 miles. Thus, hidden in its number code, is the surety that it will encompass the whole Earth.

Isaiah further described the peace and harmony of that kingdom: *"They shall not hurt nor destroy in all my holy mountain (kingdom), saith the Lord,"* (Isaiah 65:25). How beautiful to realize that the number representing beginning and eternity, 144, is used here to describe the establishment of His kingdom—the New Beginning, which will last for eternity.

> 144   *In all my holy mountain* (kingdom)
> בכל הר קדשי (multiplied)

The child that was born who would bring the New Beginning was the *Lord Jesus Christ, Κυριος Ιησους Χριστος,* 3,168. Multiply the digits (3 x 1 x 6 x 8) and the product is 144 (12²).

John, the writer of the book of Revelation, described the *"new heavens and new earth."* He called it the New Jerusalem.

> *And I saw a new heaven and a new earth...and I,*
> *John, saw the holy city, New Jerusalem, coming down*
> *from God out of heaven,* (Revelation 21:1,2).

He described the city he saw in vision as being like a giant cube, coming down and engulfing the Earth. It had three gates on each side, making 12. On each gate was inscribed the name of one of the tribes of ancient Israel, making 12. The gates faced the four cardinal directions, just as the oxen that supported the Molten Sea. Although the city was a cube, its wall was circular–or more properly, spherical. It was as if the sphere were inscribed within the cube. The square ground plan was 12,000 furlongs per side, which is 7,920,000 feet, or 1,500 miles. The dimensions of the wall are given in a different scale than the ground plan, however, we have the exact same configuration and numbers as found in the cube drawn around the Earth, and the rounded figure of 144 cubits for the wall corresponds to the circumference of Earth.

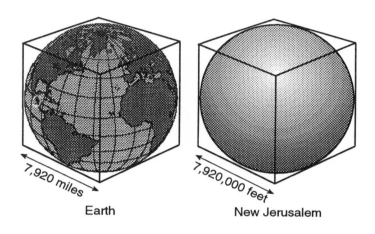

Earth   New Jerusalem

The design of each of the three witnesses will exactly overlay the Earth-Moon and the New Jerusalem design. The evidence is astounding! The design–yes, I dare call it the Sacred Design–not only bears testimony of a Designer, but of a beautiful master plan, engulfing the history and future of man.

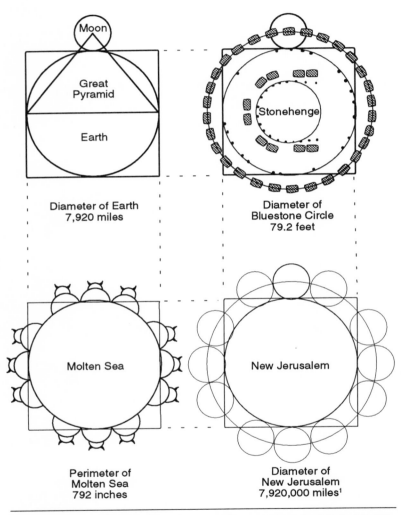

Diameter of Earth
7,920 miles

Diameter of
Bluestone Circle
79.2 feet

Perimeter of
Molten Sea
792 inches

Diameter of
New Jerusalem
7,920,000 miles[1]

1 The design of the New Jerusalem was observed by John Michell in *The Dimensions of Paradise,* Thames and Hudson, Ltd., London, 1988.

182

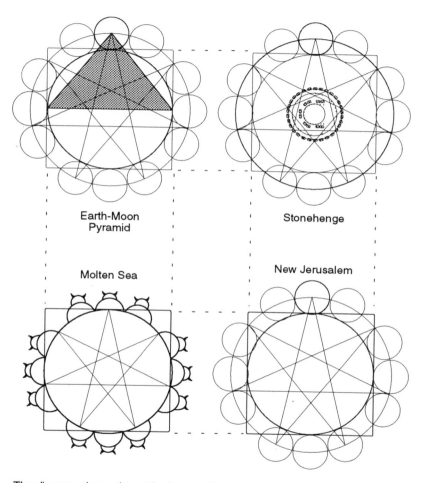

Earth-Moon Pyramid

Stonehenge

Molten Sea

New Jerusalem

The diagram above shows the Aubrey Circle of Stonehenge corresponding to the circle drawn through the center of the Moon. In the diagram on the opposite page, it is the Sarsen Circle that corresponds to the circle through the center of the Moon, while the Bluestone Circle corresponds to the circle of the Earth. Both diagrams are an accurate representation of the design of Stonehenge.

BEGINNINGS

The Apostle John, further describing the New Jerusalem, spoke of those who would enter:

And I will write on him the name of my God, and the name of the city of my God, the New Jerusalem. (Rev. 3:12)

The Greek text for the above statement is *και γραψω επ αυτον το ονομα του Θεου μου και το ονομα της πολεως του Θεου μου της καινης Ιερουσαλημ.* The total of all the letter-numbers is 10,656.

$$74 \times 144 = 10,656$$
$$12 \times 888 = 10,656$$
$$37 \times 288 = 10,656$$

When Jesus began his ministry on Earth, he chose 12 to be his special representatives. They were to be the nucleus of his followers. Their names total 10,656.

Peter	*πετρος*	755
Andrew	*Ανδρεας*	361
James	*Ιακωβος*	1,103
John	*Ιωαννης*	1,119
Philip	*Φιλιππος*	980
Nathanael	*Ναθαναηλ*	150
Levi (Matthew)	*Λευι*	445
Thomas	*Θωμας*	1,050
James (son of Alpheus)	*Ιακωβος Αλφαιου*	2,115
Lebbaeus (Thaddeus)	*Λεββαιος*	320
Simon the Canaanite	*Σιμων ο καναναιος*	1,573
Judas	*Ιουδας*	685
		10,656

They were to be the nucleus of and representatives of the holy city, the New Jerusalem. In the book of Revelation, those who represent that city are said to be 12 thousand from each of the tribes of Israel. They are listed thus:

Judah	$Iov\delta\alpha$	485
Reuben	$Pov\beta\eta v$	630
Gad	$\Gamma\alpha\delta$	8
Asher	$A\sigma\eta\rho$	309
Nepthalim	$N\epsilon\phi\theta\alpha\lambda\epsilon\iota\mu$	650
Manasses	$M\alpha\nu\alpha\sigma\sigma\eta\varsigma$	700
Simeon	$\Sigma\upsilon\mu\epsilon\omega\nu$	1,495
Levi	$\Lambda\epsilon\upsilon\iota$	445
Issachar	$I\sigma\sigma\alpha\chi\alpha\rho$	1,112
Zebulon	$Z\alpha\beta\upsilon\lambda\omega\nu$	1,360
Joseph	$I\omega\sigma\eta\phi$	1,518
Benjamin	$B\epsilon\nu\iota\alpha\mu\iota\nu$	168
		8,880

8,880 x 12,000 from each tribe = 106,560,000

The number 10,656, the number of the completed New Jerusalem, both adds and multiplies to 18 (zeros dropped). It bears the numbers of beginning and new beginning.

The Sun, the source of light, energy and life on Earth, as we have seen, aptly represents the true source of life, the *Elohim*. The solar number, 864, is also the number for *God*, $\Theta\epsilon\omega\nu$, 864. The New Jerusalem also bears the solar number.

864,000 miles – diameter of Sun
864   *God*, $\Theta\epsilon\omega\nu$
864   *Jerusalem*, $I\epsilon\rho\upsilon\sigma\alpha\lambda\eta\mu$
864   *The word of the Lord from Jerusalem* (New Jerusalem), ‏ודבר יהוה מירושלם‎ (Micah 4:2)

If we were to enclose the Sun within a cube, as the design of the New Jerusalem shows, the perimeter of the square would be 3,456,000 miles. The number 3,456, in the gematria of the Old and New Testaments, both by addition and multiplication shows the all-inclusive completeness—the ultimate magnitude—of all the works of God, from the beginning to the fullness of the New Beginning. Share with me the beauty of the numbers.

By addition:

3,456   *Alpha and Omega, the beginning and the end,* $\alpha\lambda\phi\alpha$ $\kappa\alpha\iota\ \tau o\ \Omega\ \eta\ \alpha\rho\chi\eta\ \kappa\alpha\iota\ \tau o\ \tau\epsilon\lambda o\varsigma$ (Rev. 1:8)

3,456   *The City of my God* (New Jerusalem), $\tau\eta\varsigma\ \pi o\lambda\epsilon\omega\varsigma$ $\tau o\upsilon\ \Theta\epsilon o\upsilon\ \mu o\upsilon$ (Rev. 3:12)

3,456   *The marriage of the bride and Lamb,* $o\ \gamma\alpha\mu o\varsigma\ \tau o\upsilon$ $\alpha\rho\nu\iota o\upsilon\ \kappa\alpha\iota\ \eta\ \gamma\upsilon\nu\eta\ \alpha\upsilon\tau o\upsilon$ (Rev. 19:7)

By multiplication (zeros dropped):

3,456   *His throne is in the heavens,* בשמים הכין כסאו (Psalm 103:19)

3,456   *His foundation,* יסודתו (Psalm. 87:1)

3,456   *His dominion,* בשמים הכין כסאו (Psalm 103:19)

3,456   *The sides of the north* (God's dwelling place), ירכתי צפון (Psalm 48:2)

3,456   *He who sits in the heavens,* ושב בשמים (Psalm 2:4)

3,456   *All His work* (completion of creation), כל מלאכתו (Genesis 2:3)

3,456   *All your wonderful works,* כל נפלאותיך (Psalm 26:7)

3,456   *Truth,* $\alpha\lambda\eta\theta\eta\varsigma$

The sum of the digits (3+4+5+6) is 18 – the numbers of beginning and new beginning. The multiplication of the digits (3x4x5x6) is 3,600. The circle has always been defined as 360°. This magnificent circle, representing all the works of the beginning and new beginning, multiplies to 144 (12^2).

144   *Circle,* ג x ו x ח = 144

Beginning and eternity are summed up in the Hebrew word *kedem,* קדם. The addition of its letter-numbers equals 144.

The Universe, as we know it, began about 15 billion years ago from a singularity. But the true Singularity that preceded it, is the One who bears the number 1 – the Beginner, the Designer. I stand in awe of the beauty of the Design!

Appendix 1

Elohim and the Number 37

There is ample evidence in both the Hebrew text of the Old Testament, and the Greek text of the New Testament, that the number 37 pertains to the Elohim (both Father and Son). Below is a list of some of the names, titles, and descriptions of the Elohim, whose letter-numbers add to 37 or to multiples of 37, copied from *Stonehenge and the Great Pyramid: Window on the Universe,* pages 121 to 133. The list by no means presents them all, but it is sufficient for proof that the number 37 was part of the sacred design.

37	(37 x 27 = 999 resolves to 27)
37	*God,* אלהא, (Daniel 4:2)
37	*Only Son,* היחיד
37	*Power,* אול
370	*Everlasting righteousness,* צדק לעולם, (Psalm 119:142)
370	*He lives,* שכן, (Isaiah 33:5)
37	*Only begotten,* יחידה
370	*He rules,* משל, (Psalm 66:7)
370	*God (Elohim) is my King of old,* אלהים מלכי מקדם, (Psalm 74:12)

37	*Glory,* הכבוד
370	*Whole,* שלם
370	*Whole,* ολος
370	*God (Elohim),* 86 + *God (Theos)* 284 = 370

37 x 2 = 74   (74 x 27 = 1998 resolves to 27)

74	*A great God,* אל גדול, (Psalm 95:3)
74	*Their Redeemer,* גאלם, (Jeremiah 50:34)
740	*Judge of all the earth,* השפט כל הארץ, (Genesis 18:25)
740	*Circle,* κυκλος
740	*Creation,* κτισις
74	*Foundation,* יסד
74	*Everlasting,* עד

37 x 3 = 111   (111 x 27 = 2997 resolves to 27)

111	*Wonderful,* אלפ, (Isaiah 9:6)
111	*The Most High,* עליא, (Daniel 4:32)
1110	*Only Son,* υιος μονος, (John 3:16)
1110	*The blood of Jesus,* το αιμα Ιησου, (I John 1:7)
111	*Son of the Living God,* בני אל חי, (Hosea 1:10)
111	*Lord of all,* אדון כל, (Zechariah 6:5)
111	*A precious stone,* אבן חן, (Proverbs 17:8)

37 x 4 = 148   (148 x 27 = 3996 resolves to 27)

1480	*Christ,* Χριστος
148	*The Most High,* אלהא עליא, (Daniel 4:2)
1480	*Son of God,* υιος Κυριος

37 x 5 = 185   (285 x 27 = 4995 resolves to 27)

185	*Rabbi,* ο ραββι
185	*Glory,* δοξαν
1850	*The Messiah, Word of the Father,* ο Μεσσιας Λογος Πατρος
1850	*The strong man* (representing Jesus), τον ισχυρον, (Matthew 12:29)

37 x 6 = 222   (222 x 27 = 5994 resolves to 27)

222 *The Voice of God,* קול אלהים, (Deut. 4:33)

2220 *I am Alpha and Omega, εγω Αλφα και Ωμεγα*

222 *A stone of stumbling* (referring to Jesus as the topstone), ולאבן נגף, (Isaiah 8:14)

222 *The Lord is my Rock and my shield,* יהוה עזי ומגני, (Psalm 28:7)

222 *Nazarene, Ναζαρηνε*

2220 *Unto you that fear my name shall the Sun of Righteousness arise with healing in his wings,* ומרפא בכנפיה וזרחה לכם יראי שמי שמש צדקה, (Malachi 4:2)

37 x 7 = 259   (259 x 27 = 6993 resolves to 27)

259 *Kingdom, βασιλεια*

2590 *Only Son, Christ, υιος μονος Χριστος*

2590 *The seed of David* (referring to Jesus), *οτι εκ του σπερματος Δαυιδ,* (John 7:42)

37 x 8 = 296   (296 x 27 = 7992 resolves to 27)

296 *The Rock,* צור

296 *God,* צור

296 *Only begotten, μονογενη*

2960 *Son of Man, υιος του ανθρωπου,* (Matthew 8:20)

296 *Jehovah reigns forever,* יהוה ימלך לעלם, (Exodus 15:18)

296 *The mount of God (Elohim),* הר האלהים, (Exodus 18:5)

37 x 9 = 333   (333 x 27 = 8991 resolves to 27)

333 *Thy throne O God (Elohim) is forever,* כסאך אלהים עולם, (Psalm 45:6)

3330 *Lord of lords, Κυριος των κυριων*

3330 *The will of God in Christ Jesus, θελημα Θεου εν Χριστω Ιησου,* (I Thes. 5:18)

3330 *Behold I lay in Zion a chief cornerstone* (Jesus as the topstone of the Pyramid), *ιδου τιθημι εν Σιων λιθον ακρογωνιαιον,* (I Peter 2:6)

37 x 11 = 407   (407 x 27 = 10989 resolves to 27)
407   *Lord of all the earth,* אדון כל הארץ, ((Joshua 3:13)

37 x 12 = 444   (444 x 27 = 11988 resolves to 27)
4440   *The Lord Christ,* τω Κυριω Χριστω, (Col. 3:24)
4440   *Christ the Son of Man,* Χριστος υιος του ανθρωπου
444   *Atonement,* καταλλαγην, (Romans 5:11)
444   *The Rock of my refuge,* לצור מחסי, (Psalm 94:22)

37 x 13 = 481   (481 x 27 = 12987 resolves to 27)
481   *The beginning* (or genesis) of Christ, η γενεσις,
         (Matthew 1:1)

37 x 14 = 518   (518 x 27 = 13986 resolves to 27)
518   *Sun,* ηλιου, (Mark 16:2)
518   (I am) *the Door,* η θυρα, (John 10:9)
5180   *The stone which the builders rejected, the same is
         become the head of the corner,* λιθον ον απεδοκιμασαν
         οι οικοδομουντες ουτος εγενηθη εις κεφαλην
         γωνιας, (Luke 20:17)
5180   *The Father sent the Son to be the Saviour of the world,*
         ο πατηρ απεσταλκεν τον υιον σωτηρα του κοσμου,
         (I John 4:14)

37 x 15 = 555   (555 x 27 = 14985 resolves to 27)
5550   *Our Lord and his Christ,* Κυριου ημων και του
         Χριστου αυτου, (Revelation 11:15)
555   *Power,* δυναμιν

37 x 16 = 592   (592 x 27 = 15984 resolves to 27)
592   *Godhead,* Θεοτης
592   *The Lord of heaven,* מרא שמיא, (Daniel 5:23)
592   *Holiness,* αγιοτης
592   *The Holy One of Jacob,* קדוש יעקב, (Isaiah 29:23)

37 x 17 = 629   (629 x 27 = 16983 resolves to 27)

629   *The true Word,* $\alpha\lambda\eta\theta\eta\varsigma\ \Lambda o\gamma o\varsigma$

37 x 18 = 666   (666 x 27 = 17982 resolves to 27)

666   *The head of the corner,* לראש פנה, (Psalm 118:22)

666   *Jehovah God that created the heavens,* יהוה בורא השמים
       האל, (Isaiah 42:5)

666   *He hath made the earth,* עשה ארץ, (Jeremiah 10:12)

666   *Let there be lights,* יהי מארת, (Genesis 1:14)

37 x 19 = 703   (703 x 27 = 18981 resolves to 27)

703   *The God of Israel,* $o\ \Theta\varepsilon o\varsigma\ I\sigma\rho\alpha\eta\lambda$

703   *The Holy One of Israel,* $o\ \alpha\gamma\iota o\sigma\ I\sigma\rho\alpha\eta\lambda$

703   *The God of David,* $\Theta\varepsilon o\varsigma\ \Delta\alpha\upsilon\iota\delta$

37 x 21 = 777   (777 x 27 = 20979 resolves to 27)

777   *The man child,* $\tau o\nu\ \alpha\rho\sigma\varepsilon\nu\alpha$, (Revelation 12:13)

777   *I* (Jehovah) *have raised him* (Jesus) *up,* אנכי העירתהו,
       (Isaiah 45:13)

37 x 22 = 814   (814 x 27 = 21978 resolves to 27)

814   *The powerful Word* (of God), $o\ \lambda o\gamma o\varsigma\ \varepsilon\nu\varepsilon\rho\gamma\eta\varsigma$,
       (Hebrews 4:12)

814   *God,* $\Theta\varepsilon\omega$, (Mark 10:27)

814   *His throne as the sun before me,* כסאו כשמש נגדי, (Psalm
       89:36)

37 x 24 = 888   (888 x 27 = 23976 resolves to 27)

888   *Jesus,* $I\eta\sigma o\upsilon\varsigma$

888   *The Founder,* $o\ o\iota\kappa\iota\sigma\tau\eta\varsigma$

888   *I am the life,* $\varepsilon\iota\mu\iota\ \eta\ \zeta\omega\eta$

888   *Thou Lord art exalted forever,* אתה מרום לעלם יהוה,
       (Psalm 92:8)

888   *Salvation of our God,* ישועת אלהינו, (Isaiah 52:10)

8880   *An ark, in which a few, that is eight souls were saved through water* (the ark pictured salvation through Jesus), κιβωτου εις ην ολιγοι τουτ εστιν οκτω ψυχαι διεσωθησαν δι υδατος, (I Peter 3:20)

8880   *Behold, a virgin shall conceive and bear a son, and they will call his name Emmanuel, which being interpreted is God with us,* ιδου η παρθενος εν γαστρι εξει και τεξεται υιον και καλεσουσιν ονομα αυτου Εμμανουηλ ο εστιν μεθερμηνευομενον μεθ ημων Θεος, (Matthew 1:23)

888   *I am Jehovah, I change not,* אני יהוה לא שניתי, (Malachi 3:6)

37 x 26 = 962   (962 x 27 = 25974 resolves to 27)

962   *Jehovah-shalom,* שלם, 370 x יהוה, 26 = 9620

962   *Godhead,* Θεοτητος, (Col. 2:9)

962   *Thou art clothed with honor and majesty,* והדר לבשת הוד, (Psalm 104:1)

962   *Forever O Lord thy Word is settled in heaven,* בשמים לעולם יהוה דברך נצב, (Psalm 119:89)

37 x 27 = 999   (999 x 27 = 26973 resolves to 27)

999   *In the beginning God (Elohim),* בראשית אלהים, (Genesis 1:1)

999   *Glory of God,* δοξαν Θεω, (Romans 4:20)

999   *A door of hope,* פתח תקוה, (Hosea 2:15)

37 x 28 = 1036   (1036 x 27 = 27972 resolves to 27)

1036   *God and the Lamb,* ο Θεος και το αρνιον (Rev. 21:23, *The glory of God did lighten it, and the Lamb is the light thereof.*)

1036   *I am the resurrection,* ειμι η αναστασις, (John 11:25)

37 x 29 = 1073   (1073 x 27 = 28971 resolves to 27)

1073   *The God of the earth,* ο Θεος της γης, (Genesis 24:3, Septuagint)

37 x 31 = 1147   (1147 x 27 = 30969 resolves to 27)

1147   *The will of God, θελημοτος Θεου,* (Romans 15:32)

37 x 32 = 1184   (1184 x 27 = 31968 resolves to 27)

1184   *Chief cornerstone, ακρογωνιαιον,* (I Peter 2:6)

1184   *Throne of God, θρονου Θεου,* (Revelation 22:1)

1184   *In a different form, εν ετερα μορφη,* (Jesus, after his resurrection appeared *"in a different form"* to his disciples on the road to Emmaus), (Mark 16:12)

37 x 33 = 1221   (1221 x 27 = 32967 resolves to 27)

1221   *Wonderful, Θαυμαστος,* (the prophetic name of Jesus in Isaiah 9:6—Septuagint)

1221   *Carca*se (the humanity of Jesus as man's ransom price), *πτωμα,* (Matthew 24:28)

1221   *His feet shall stand in that day upon the Mount of Olives,* (prophetic of the return of Christ), על הר הזיתים עמדו רגליו ביום ההוא, (Zechariah 14:4)

1221   *Holy Master, δεσποτησ ο αγιος,* (Revelation 6:10)

37 x 36 = 1332   (1332 x 27 = 35964 resolves to 27)

1332   *Alpha, Omega* (first and last), *αλφα ω*

1332   *True God, αληθως Θεος*

1332   *Behold your King* (Jesus), *ιδου βασιλευς,* (John 12:15)

37 x 37 = 1369   1369 x 27 = 36963 resolves to 27)

1369   *Image of God, εικων Θεου,* (II Corinthians 4:4)

1369   *The God of life, ο Θεος ζωης*

1369   *The Son of David* (Jesus), *ο υιου Δαυιδ,* (Matthew 1:1)

37 x 39 = 1443   (1443 x 27 = 38961 resolves to 27)

1443   *The Word of the Lord, ο λογος Κυριου*

1443   *The peace of God, η ειρηνη του Θεου,* (Phil. 4:7)

37 x 42 = 1554   (1554 x 27 = 41958 resolves to 27)

1554   *Only Word of the Father, μονος λογος πατρος*
1554   *My beloved Son, υιον μου αγαπητον,* (Luke 10:13)
1554   *We have found the Messiah, ευρηκαμεν τον Μεσσιαν,*
       (John 1:41)

37 x 43 = 1591   (1591 x 27 = 42957 resolves to 27)

1591   *Spirit of life, πνευμα ζωης*
1591   *I am the Good Shepherd, εγω ειμι ο ποιμην ο καλος,*
       (John 10:11)

37 x 44 = 1628   (1628 x 27 = 43956 resolves to 9)

1628   *The head of the corner* (referring to Jesus as the
       topstone), *κεφαλη γωνιας,* (Matthew 21:42)
1628   *Son of David* (Jesus), *υιω Δαυιδ,* (Matthew 21:15)

37 x 45 = 1665   (1665 x 27 = 44955 resolves to 27)

1665   *The mouth of God, στοματος Θεου,* (Matthew 4:4)

37 x 46 = 1702   (1702 x 27 = 45954 resolves to 27)

1702   *Peace of the Father, ειρηνη του πατρος*
1702   *Jacob's well* (from which Jesus drank), *πηγη του Ιακωβ,*
       (John 4:6)

37 x 47 = 1739   (1739 x 27 = 45953 resolves to 27)

1739   *Christ Kingdom, Χριστος βασιλεια*

37 x 48 = 1776   (1776 x 27 = 47952 resolves to 27)

1776   *Lord of the sabbath, Κυριος σαββατου,* (Mark 2:28)
1776   *River of life, ποταμος ζωης,* (Revelation 22:1)
1776   (1778) *I came forth from the Father, εξηλθον εκ του
       πατρος,* (John 16:28)
1776   *The Lamb in the midst of the throne, οτι αρνιον ανα
       μεσον θρονου,* (Revelation 7:17)

37 x 49 = 1813   (1813 x 27 = 48951 resolves to 27)
1813   *Lord of hosts, Κυριος σαβαωθ,* (Septuagint)
1813   *Emmanuel, the Son of David, Εμμανουηλ ο υιος Δαυιδ*

37 x 51 = 1887   (1887 x 27 = 50949 resolves to 27)
1887   *The Father and the Son, τον πατερα και τον υιον,* (I John 2:22)
1887   *The One from heaven, εκ του ουρανου,* (John 3:13)

37 x 52 = 1924   (1924 x 27 = 51948 resolves to 27)
1924   *The God of the universe, ο Θεου του κοσμος*

37 x 53 = 1961   (1961 x 27 = 52947 resolves to 27)
1961   *The cornerstone, ο λιθος της γωνιας*

37 x 54 = 1998   (1998 x 27 = 53946 resolves to 27)
1998   *The son of the virgin, ο υιος εκ της παρθενου*
1998   *His only begotten Son, υιον αυτου μονογενη,* (I John 4:9)

37 x 55 = 2035   (2035 x 27 = 54945 resolves to 27)
2035   *Christ in you, Χριστος εν υμιν,* (Col. 1:27)
2035   *Wisdom of God* (used as a metaphor of Jesus), *σοφια του Θεου,* (Ephesians 3:10; I Cor. 1:24)
2035   *The righteousness of God* (used as a metaphor of Jesus), *η δικαιοσυνη του Θεου,* (II Pet. 1:1; Rom. 10:3)

37 x 56 = 2072   (2072 x 27 = 55944 resolves to 27)
2072   *The Alpha, the Omega* (the first, the last), *το αλφα το ω,* (Rev. 1:8)

37 x 57 = 2109   (2109 x 27 = 56943 resolves to 27)

2109   *Heir of the Kingdom of God, κληρονομος της βασιλειας Θεου*

2109   *He that sat upon the horse* (The King of kings and Lord of lords) *καθημενου επι του ιππου,* (Rev. 19:21)

37 x 59 = 2183   (2183 x 27 = 58941 resolves to 27)

2183   *The right hand of God, δεξιων του Θεου,* (Acts 7:55)

2183   *Christ the Holy One of Israel, Χριστος ο αγιος Ισραηλ*

2183   *Head over all things to the church* (referring to Jesus), *κεφαλη υπερ παντα τη εκκλησια,* (Eph. 1:22)

37 x 61 = 2257   (2257 x 27 = 60939 resolves to 27)

2257   *Gospel of Christ, ευαγγελιον Χριστου*

2257   *Noah's Ark* (an illustration of salvation through Christ), *κιβωτος Νωε*

37 x 62 = 2294   (2294 x 27 = 61938 resolves to 27)

2294   *His life* (Christ's), *τη ζωη αυτου,* (Rom. 5:10)

37 x 63 = 2331   (2331 x 27 = 62937 resolves to 27)

2331   *This Jesus hath God raised up, τον Ιησουν ανεστησεν ο Θεος,* (Acts 2:32)

37 x 64 = 2368   (2368 x 27 = 63936 resolves to 27)

2368   *Jesus Christ* (it can be spelled *Ιησους Χριστος* or *Ιησου Χριστου,* depending on its placement in the sentence, but it still adds to 2368)

2368   *Him for whom are all things* (Jesus), *αυτω δι ον τα παντα,* (Heb. 2:10)

37 x 66 = 2442   (2442 x 27 = 65934 resolves to 27)

2442   *The Son of God, τη υιου του Θεου,* (Gal. 2:20)

2442   *Jesus, the name given by the angel, Ιησους το κληθεν υπο αγγελου,* (Luke 2:21)

37 x 69 = 2553   (2553 x 27 = 68931 resolves to 27)
2553   *Name of the only begotten Son of God, ονομα*
       μονογενους υιου Θεου, (John 3:18)

37 x 72 = 2664   (2664 x 27 = 71928 resolves to 27)
2664   *The Lord God is one Lord, Κυριος Θεος εις εστιν,*
       κυριος, (Mark 12:29)

37 x 73 = 2701   (2701 x 27 = 72927 resolves to 27)
2701   *The grace of Christ, χαριτι Χριστου,* (Gal. 1:6)
2701   *In the beginning God created the heaven and the earth,*
       בראשית אלהים ברא את השמים ואת הארץ(Gen. 1:1)

37 x 75 = 2775   (2775 x 27 = 74925 resolves to 27)
2775   *The Prince of Life* (Jesus), *τον αρχηγον της ζωης,*
       (Acts 3:15)

37 x 76 = 2812   (2812 x 27 = 75924 resolves to 27)
2812   *His eternal power and Godhead, η αιδιος αυτου*
       δυναμις και Θειοτης, (Rom. 1:20)
2812   *Blood of Christ, αιματι του Χριστου,* (Eph. 2:13)
2812   *Eternal redemption, αιωνιαν λυτρωσιν,* (Heb. 9:12)

37 x 85 = 3145   (3145 x 27 = 84915 resolves to 27)
3145   *Lord of heaven and earth, Κυριε του ουρανου και*
       της γης, (Luke 10:21)

37 x 86 = 3182   (3182 x 27 = 85914 resolves to 27)
3182   *The Lion of the tribe of Judah* (Jesus), *ο λεων ο εκ της*
       φυλης Ιουδα, (Rev. 5:5)

37 x 91 = 3367   (3367 x 27 = 90909 resolves to 27)
3367   *Father of spirits, πατρι των πνευματων,* (Heb. 12:9)

37 x 92 = 3404   (3404 x 27 = 91908 resolves to 27)

3404   *His divine power, της θειας δυναμεως αυτου*, (II Pet. 1:3)

37 x 93 = 3441   (3441 x 27 = 92907 resolves to 27)

3441   *The riches of His glory, τον πλουτον της δοξης αυτου*, (Rom. 9:23)

3441   *A High Priest after the order of Melchizedek* (Jesus), *αρχιερευς κατα την ταξιν Μελχισεδεκ*, (Heb. 5:10)

37 x 95 = 3515   (3515 x 27 = 94905 resolves to 27)

3515   *The spirit of Jesus Christ, πνευματος Ιησου Χριστου*, (Phil 1:19)

37 x 96 = 3552   (3552 x 27 = 95904 resolves to 27)

3552   *Author of eternal salvation, αιτιος σωτηριας αιωνιου*, (Heb. 5:9)

3552   *The mystery of God, του μυστηριου του Θεου*, (Col. 2:2)

37 x 98 = 3626   (3626 x 27 = 97902 resolves to 27)

3626   *This is my body* (Christ's), *τουτο εστιν το σωμα μου*, (Matt. 26:26)

37 x 101 = 3737   (3737 x 27 = 100899 resolves to 27)

3737   *Jesus Christ the son of David, Ιησου Χριστου ο υιου Δαυιδ*, (Matt. 1:1)

3737   *The God of our fathers, ο Θεος των πατερων ημων*, (Acts 22:14)

37 x 102 = 3774   (3774 x 27 = 101898 resolves to 27)

3774   *The Messiah, the Saviour of the world, ο Μεσσιας ο σωτηρ του κοσμου*

3774   *The God of heaven, τω Θεω του ουρανου*, (Rev. 11:13)

37 x 103 = 3811   (3811 x 27 = 102897 resolves to 27)

3811   *The person of Christ, προσωπω Χριστου,* (II Cor. 2:10)

37 x 109 = 4033   (4033 x 27 = 108891 resolves to 27)

4033   *The firstborn of all creation, πρωτοτοκος πασης κτισεως,* (Col. 1:15)

37 x 115 = 4255   (4255 x 27 = 114885 resolves to 27)

4255   *The firstborn from the dead,* (the resurrected Jesus), *ο πρωτοτοκος των νεκρων,* (Rev. 1:5)

37 x 122 = 4551   (4551 x 27 = 122877 resolves to 27)

4551   *Jesus standing on the right hand of God, Ιησουν εστωτα εκ δεξιων του Θεου,* (Acts 7:55)

37 x 124 = 4588   (4588 x 27 = 123876 resolves to 27)

4588   *The Prince of the kings of the earth* (Jesus), *ο αρχων των βασιλεων της γης,* (Rev. 1:5)

37 x 131 = 4847   (4847 x 27 = 130869 resolves to 27)

4847   *God, who quickeneth all things, του Θεου του ζωογονουν τος τα παντα,* (I Tim. 6:13)

37 x 144 = 5328   (5328 x 27 = 143856 resolves to 27)

5328   (5330) *The right hand of the throne of the Majesty in the heavens, δεξια του θρονου της μεγαλωσυνης εν τοις ουρανιος,* (Heb. 8:1)

37 x 223 = 8251   (8251 x 27 = 222777 resolves to 27)

8251   *In him was life, and the life was the light of men, εν αυτω ζωη ην, και η ζωη ην το φως των ανθρωπων,* (John 1:4)

Appendix 2

The 144 Thousand on Mount Zion

The number 144 thousand appears twice in the book of Revelation. Some students of Revelation believe it is a literal number, and describes a precise quantity; others, reasoning that Revelation is a book of symbols, believe it is a symbolic number. I suggest yet a third possibility: It appears to be an *identification* number . The two uses of this number in Revelation are as follows:

> *And I heard the number of them which were sealed: and there were sealed an hundred and forty and four thousand of all the tribes of the children of Israel.* (Revelation 7:4 KJV)

> *And I looked, and, lo, a Lamb stood on the Mount Zion, and with him an hundred forty and four thousand, having his Father's name written in their foreheads.* (Revelation 14:1 KJV)

The earliest manuscripts of the book of Revelation use gematria for this number, stating it as $\rho\mu\delta$ (ρ=100 + μ=40 + δ=4), followed by the word *"thousands."*

Below is an overview of the uses of the number 144 in the gematria of the scriptures which pertain to this group.

1440	*Believers, πιστων,* (I Tim. 4:12)
144	*The Elect, η εκλογη,* (Rom. 11:7)
1440	*Elect of God, εκλογην του Θεου,* (Rom. 9:11)
1440	*Purchased firstfruits, ηγορασθησαν απαρχη,* (Rev. 14:4)
144	*Divine nature, θειον,* (Acts 17:29)
144	*Everlasting,* קדם, (Hab. 1:12)
1440	*All who have been baptized, οτι οσοι εβαπτισθημεν,* (Rom. 6:3)
144x2	*A holy calling, κλησει αγια,* (II Tim. 1:9)
144x3	*A new name* (given to the overcomers), *ονομα καινον,* (Rev. 2:17)
144x6	*Saints, αγιων,* (Rev. 8:3)
144x6	*The flock of God, ποιμνιον Θεου,* (I Pet. 5:2)
144x8	*(Those) whom thou hast given me, δεδωκας μοι,* (John 17:24)
144x9	*Now are ye God's people, νυν δε λαος Θεου,* (I Pet. 2:10)
144x11	*Priests of God, ιερεις του Θεου,* (Rev. 20:6)
144x11	*In Isaac shall thy seed be called, εν Ισαακ κληθησεται σοι σπερμα,* (Rom. 9:7)
144x12	*Living sacrifice, θυσιαν ζωσαν,* (Rom. 12:1)
144x15	*The flock, τω ποιμνιω,* (Acts 20:28)
144x15	*Chosen,* בחור
144x17	*The eternal inheritance, της αιωνιου κληρονομιας,* (Heb. 9:15)
144x18	*Gather the wheat into the barn, συναγαγειν τον σιτον εις την αποθηκην,* (Luke 3:17)
144x18	*Body of Christ, σωμα ο Χριστος,* (I Cor. 12:12)
144x20	*The Bride, the Lamb's wife, την νυμφην ψην γυναικα αρνιου,* (Rev. 21:9)

144x23 *The heavenly gift,* της δωρεας της επουρανιου, (Heb. 9:15)

144x24 *The marriage of the Lamb and His bride,* ο γαμος του αρνιου και η γυνη αυτου *(Rev. 19:7)*

144x27 *The Holy City, the New Jerusalem, coming down out of heaven,* πολιν την αγιαν Ιερουσαλημ καινην καταβαινουσαν εκ ουρανου, *(Rev. 21:2)*

144x31 *The promise of life in Christ Jesus,* επαγγελιαν ζωης της εν Χρισψω Ιησου, *(II Tim. 1:1)*

144x32 *The marriage of the Lamb has come, and His bride has made herself ready,* οτι ηλθεν ο γαμος απνιου και γυνη αυτου ητοιμασεν εαυτην, *(Rev. 19:7)*

144x54 *Church not having spot or wrinkle or any such thing, that it may be holy and unblemished,* εκκλησιαν μη εχουσαν σπιλον η ρυτιδα η ψι των τολουτων αλλ ινα η αγια και αμωμος, *(Eph. 5:27)*

144x54 *And I appoint unto you a kingdom, as my Father hath appointed unto me; that ye may eat and drink at my table in my kingdom,* καγω διατιθεμαι υμιν καθως διεθετο μοι πατηρ μου βασιλειαν ινα εσθητε και πινητε επι τραπεζης μου εν βασιλεια μου, *(Luke 22:29-30)*

144x70 *And they sing the song of Moses, the servant of God, and the song of the Lamb,* και αδουσιν την ωδην Μωυσεως του δουλου του Θεου και την ωδην του αρνιου, *(Rev. 15:3)*

144x74 *And I will write on him the name of my God, and the name of the City of my God, the New Jerusalem,* και γραψω επ αυτον το ονομα του Θεου

μου και το ονομα της πολεως του Θεου μου
της καινης Ιερουσαλημ, (Rev. 3:12)

144x79 *For as the body is one, and hath many members,
and all the members of that one body, being many,
are one body: so also is Christ,* καθαπερ γαρ το
σωμα εν εστιν και μελη πολλα εχει παντα δε
τα μελη σωματος πολλα οντα εν εστιν σωμα
ουτως και ο Χριατος (I Cor. 12:12)

From the above use of gematria, it appears that the number 144 represents that group of faithful believers who have the joy of standing with the Lamb in heavenly Zion. Or, stated differently, 144 is their identification number. John said, *"I heard the number of them which were sealed."* He did not see a quantity which he counted; he merely heard their identification number, which was 144. The word *"number"* in this verse is the Greek word αριθμος, which means a fixed number. Further in the text, John looked and saw a great multitude which no man could number. Here the word *"number"* is from the Greek word αριθμησαι, meaning to count.

There were *"thousands"* who bore the identification number of 144. Then the symbol is carried to the next verse which states that he heard 12 *"thousands"* from each tribe of Israel. Again the number is an identification number rather than a quantity. Twelve is the identifying number for Israel; it is also the identifying number for the believers whose foundation was the 12 Apostles.

Some have wondered why John's list of the 12 tribes of Israel in Revelation 7 does not precisely match the Old Testament list. I believe the reason lies in the gematria, and the meaning of the identifying numbers. The list, as given in Revelation, is shown on page 185 along with the gematria for each of the names as they appear in Thayer's Greek Lexicon. We saw that they total 8,880. Multiplying this by 12,000 from each tribe gives 106,560,000 – the number that identifies the completed New Jerusalem.

The number 10,656 also identifies the foundation of all belief in Christ – the 12 Apostles. On page 184 I showed the list of these names with the gematria for each, according to their Greek spelling. They totalled 10,656. It was not a coincidence, it was the planning of a Master Designer, for if we multiply the number for *Jesus* (888), by the number for *foundation* (74), the product will be 10,656.

Looking again at John's vision in the book of Revelation, it tells that after he *heard* the number of those standing with the Lamb, he turned and looked. But what he saw was a crowd so large that it would be impossible for him to count how many were in it. He simply called it a *great multitude*. But they still bore the same identification number, 144.

144x42   *A great multitude which no man could number, from every nation,* οχλος πολυς ον αριθμησαι αυτον ουδεις εδυνατο εκ παντος εθνους (Rev. 7:9)

144x13   *These clothed in white robes,* περιβεβλημενοι στολας λευκας (Rev. 7:13)

144x28   *These are they which came out of great tribulation,* ερχομενοι εκ της θλιψεως της μεγαλης (Rev. 7:14)

This great multitude stood *"before the throne,"* (verses 9 and 15) – the same place where he had seen the 144 thousands standing in 14:3. *"And they sung as it were a new song before the throne...and no man could learn that song but the*

144 thousands, which were redeemed from the earth.... These were redeemed from among men, the firstfruits unto God and to the Lamb...for they are without fault before the throne of God." It appears to be two descriptions of the same group who stand before the throne of God, and their identification number is 144.

Bibliography and Recommended Reading

J. Bronowski, *The Ascent of Man,* Little, Brown and Company, New York, 1973

E. W. Bullinger, *Number in Scripture,* Kregel, Grand Rapids, 1981

Tobias Dantzig, *Number, the Language of Science,* Doubleday, Garden City, NY, 1956

O.A.W. Dilke, *Mathematics and Measurement,* British Museum Publications, London, 1987

Bonnie Gaunt, *Stonehenge...a closer look,* 1979
The Magnificent Numbers of the Great Pyramid and Stonehenge, 1985
The Stones Cry Out, 1991
Stonehenge and the Great Pyramid: Window on the Universe, 1993
Bonnie Gaunt, Jackson, MI

John Gribbin, *In The Beginning,* Little, Brown and Company, New York, 1993

Stephen Hawking, *Black Holes and Baby Universes,* Bantam Books, New York, 1993
A Brief History of Time, Bantam Books, New York, 1988

James E. Horigan, *Chance or Design,* Philosophical Library, New York, 1979

John Ivimy, *The Sphinx and the Megaliths,* Turnstone, 1974

Roger S. Jones, *Physics for the Rest of Us,* Contemporary Books Chicago, 1992

Robert Lawlor, *Sacred Geometry,* Crossroad, New York, 1982

Jerry Lucas and Del Washburn, *Theomatics,* Stein and Day, New York, 1977

John Michell, *The Dimensions of Paradise,* Thames and Hudson, London, 1988

Neil Pinter, *The Eternal Question: Does God Exist?,* Neil Pinter, Borger, Texas, 1991

Gerald L. Schroeder, Ph.D., *Genesis and the Big Bang,* Bantam Books, New York, 1990

Joseph A. Seiss, *Gospel in the Stars,* Kregel, Grand Rapids, 1972

George Smoot, *Wrinkles in Time,* William Morrow and Company, New York, 1993

David L. Teuling, *For a Sign and a Witness,* Artesian Books, Muskegon, MI, 1988

Robert Williams, *The Geometrical Foundation of Natural Structure,* Dover Publications, New York, 1972

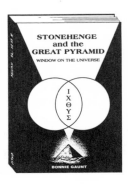

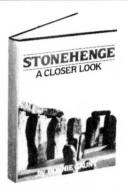